DATE DUE

NOV 4 1985

Current Trends in Science Education

Current Trends in Science Education

J. STANLEY MARSHALL
The Florida State University

ERNEST BURKMAN
The Florida State University

THE CENTER FOR APPLIED RESEARCH IN EDUCATION, INC.
New York

LIBRARY OF CONGRESS
CATALOG CARD NO.: 66–15220

PRINTED IN THE UNITED STATES OF AMERICA

Foreword

It has been said that those who live in the midst of revolution are the least sensitive to it and to the profound changes which result. In the first half of this century we saw a cultural revolution which began slowly toward the close of the 19th Century and then accelerated at a pace to almost overwhelm mankind. Today we are deep in the vortex of a social milieu which is dominated by science and technology. It is reasonable to assume that not in the foreseeable future will these forces lessen their influence on the world in which we live.

Science is something more than a subject in the curriculum. It is a quest for explanations of the perplexities which beset man as he attempts to adjust to his environment. It begins in the cradle and follows to the end. In this quest for answers, new knowledge is inevitably discovered and new patterns of relationship for older knowledge are found. As scientists have sought to explain events, a peculiar mode of inquiry has evolved which, in its essence, is experimental. This has become an effective way of getting better explanations.

The processes of inquiry through which the scientist probes his environment involve many facets—observation, classification, hypothesis, analysis, synthesis, interpretation and generalization among others. Thus, the discovery of new truth is both product and process, each being of equal importance. If either be mastered to the want of the other, true and lasting learning has not resulted.

If young people are to live fully and abundantly in a society that is strongly influenced by science and technology, they must have a real understanding of these forces and be able to use them to full advantage. Science must be learned but the learning must be more than just learning *about* science; it must be a full and rich experiencing of the broad spectrum of fact, principle and concept together with the processes by which they were discovered. Young people must learn science from teachers who have a deep understanding of

v

it as an intellectual enterprise. Under such teachers the learning process must be experienced deeply so that it becomes a way of life for the students whether they are to be artists, lawyers, truck drivers, ministers of the gospel or in any other walk of life.

Educational leaders—especially school administrators—must play leadership roles in fostering and promoting the kind of science teaching that will prepare young people for the high level of scientific literacy needed in this Age of Science. This volume is a rich source-book of ideas as well as a practical suggestion guide for those setting up modern science programs in today's schools.

ELLSWORTH S. OBOURN
Specialist for Science
Department of Health, Education
and Welfare

Current Trends in Science Education

J. Stanley Marshall

Ernest Burkman

The curriculum revision movement in the United States is now in full swing. The present movement got under way in physics and spread to biology and chemistry, and now extends to the earth sciences. The impact of the movement has been felt not only on the curriculum of the secondary school but also in teacher education. Its peripheral influence is felt on all other school subjects. *Current Trends in Science Education* is a clear explanation of why curriculum revision is necessary in the first place and what changes have resulted in biology, chemistry, physics and the earth sciences. It also depicts the changes in the field of teacher education. A major contribution of the book is its raising several very pertinent questions about the new programs in science.

Marshall and Burkman discuss their subject in a very workman-like manner. In *each* of the sciences they begin by discussing the need for change in the teaching of that science. They discuss the inadequacies in the traditional courses and point the way to the needed change. Their discussion of the Biological Curriculum Study is typical of the approach they use. They set forth the criticism of professional biologists, the sterility of the traditionally taught courses and the need for an approach to biology which is more scientific and less natural history. The authors are sympathetic to the traditional approach but at the same time they present an honest and fair criticism of it along with the reasons for change which they feel to be necessary.

The curriculum revision movement in science education has taken into account, possibly more than in any other field, the need to train teachers. This book depicts the efforts made by the National Science Foundation to improve teacher education and also discusses some of the changes American universities have made in graduate study programs.

New programs in science education have solved many curriculum problems but new problems have been created. Do students really learn what is intended by the new program is a question raised and discussed by the authors. They point out that not all students learn more science merely because they are in a new science program. They present clearly the problems of coordination and integration within the sciences and with other subjects—a matter of extension of the science curriculum revision movement into the colleges and the elementary schools.

In a period of general curriculum revision in American education, the work in the field of science has been exemplary. And this book discusses these significant happenings eloquently. Marshall and Burkman's *Current Trends in Science Education* is a book that should be read by all engaged in secondary school education.

DANIEL E. GRIFFITHS
Content Editor

Contents

CHAPTER IV

Chemistry: The Many Faces of Structure 47

CHAPTER V

The Ninth Grade Course In Science: A Dilemma 67

CHAPTER VI

Needed: A Modern Teacher For Modern Science 80

CHAPTER VII

Remaining Problems in Secondary-School Science

CHAPTER I

The Problem: What Should Be Taught?

The prime perplexity which faces those concerned with curriculum development at this point in history is how to cope with an abundance of potentially valuable curriculum content. Where only a few years ago, the typical high school teacher attempted to "cover" his subject, the great volume of information presently available in all areas makes this unthinkable as an educational objective today—unless, of course, one is satisfied with serious distortions due to superficiality.

The present information crisis has become particularly acute in the area of science. Not only has a vast storehouse of scientific ideas been accumulated, but the *rate* of increase in knowledge has accelerated to staggering proportions. We are told that the amount of scientific information available is now being doubled every ten years. The crisis which this situation presents shows no sign of lessening since the number of scientists active today is greater than the total number that has lived up to the present time.

With this situation facing us, it is obvious that one who would develop science curriculum today must select the content of his course very carefully. But what shall be the basis for such selection? Should the course planner incorporate those aspects of science which seem to have greatest utility in the everyday lives of the students for which the instruction is intended? Should he ignore practical matters and select content in terms of its disciplinary significance? Or should he include those portions of the subject which seem to have the greatest potential for affecting the students' thought processes? All of these points of view have been reflected as objectives for science teaching in the past, and all are defended vigorously today in various parts of the educational world. During the past few years, however, a rather definite trend has been apparent in the approach to content selection. As a result, although many types of science courses are still taught in the United States, certain approaches are clearly in the ascendency.

The Bases for Science Content Selection

If one seriously pursues the question of what content should be included in a science course, he is immediately faced by the question, "What is to be accomplished as a result of the instruction?" Any analysis of the purposes of science teaching must consider at least three factors.

In the first place, obviously the present nature of the subject must be a vital consideration in what should be taught. Few, if any, would advocate the teaching of outmoded or inaccurate concepts. Secondly, since the science must be taught to somebody, the nature of the learner for whom the instruction is intended takes on considerable importance particularly with respect to our understanding of the mental processes involved in the learning of science. Finally, the question of what the student will do with the knowledge obtained must be faced. One cannot ignore the fact that the student lives in a real world and therefore the nature of that world has a profound influence on the problem of what should be taught.

Even if these factors were to remain constant the problem of curriculum construction would be difficult. Unfortunately, in the case of science, the constant state of flux of these bases greatly complicates the situation. Our understanding of science and of learning has changed radically in recent years. And, perhaps most importantly, the society of today bears little resemblance to that of thirty years ago. These shifts in science, learning theory, and society have led to what has been termed by many the current "revolution in science teaching." Let us now try to analyze present thinking in these areas and see how it is affecting the secondary school science program.

The Nature of Modern Science

Many people look upon the scientist essentially as one who describes nature by careful observations, and upon the scientific process as the accumulation of his descriptions which, based on direct observation, represent "irrevocable fact."

This conception is in part correct. As a matter of fact, almost all science begins with observation. In many of the sciences, several hundred years were devoted to the accumulation of a large volume of observed descriptions of nature and some scientists are still confined largely to this type of work. To the scientist, however, his discipline "grows up" when it allows him to ascertain relationships between some of the observations made and thereby go beyond the information obtained through the senses. The usual result of this process is an abstract mental picture which tends to see nature in an orderly, though man-made, pattern. This, of course, is the stuff of which scientific theories are made. In essence, the scientist constantly seeks to alter his questions from *"what* is the situation?" to "can I find similarities which might give a hint at to *why* this situation exists?" When he can begin to provide answers to the latter question, he considers himself to have been most successful.

Many of the most important aspects of science have nothing to do with microscopes, test tubes, telescopes, atom smashers, or acids. Such things are often important since they are useful tools in collecting the information about nature without which the scientist cannot operate. The scientist makes his major "discoveries," however, when he leaves his laboratory, contemplates his measurements, and says to himself, "what does this mean?" The important ideas contributed by such men as Darwin, Einstein, Rutherford, Fermi, and the vast majority of well-known scientists resulted from this sort of mental effort.

Science, then, as it matures, tends to proceed from the practical to the theoretical. It moves from preoccupation with concrete objects to the development of abstractions which relate objects and events, one to another. Unfortunately, in much of traditional science teaching little or no distinction has been made between the results of measuring and observing things (scientific facts) and the principles of science which are in reality only mental pictures (the abstractions mentioned above) but which have the greater power in opening new doors of understanding. Traditional teaching has lead to serious misconceptions in terms of both science content and the nature of science itself.

As an example, when the average high school graduate is asked to give his conception of an atom, he is likely to respond with a very precise and careful description of an object composed of a nucleus made up of protons and neutrons with other particles called electrons traveling around it in discrete orbits. On the other hand, when the chemist is asked the same question, his answer is likely to be punctuated with statements like "I think," "Perhaps," "Maybe," or

"Our present thought is." In this situation the high school student is talking about atoms as if they had actually been observed and measured, while the chemist realizes that the atomic theory is the chemist's way of organizing a large number of indirect observations into a meaningful pattern. The scientist also realizes that it is possible to arrange these same observations into several descriptions of the atom, all of which explain some of the atom's behavior and characteristics and none of which explains them all. To the high school student the subject is closed when he gives the answer above. To the chemist the nature of atoms is a lively question, more unanswered than answered.

Our high school student is likely to be shocked if he discovers that atoms are described quite differently ten years later. In fact, he is likely to lose confidence in scientists and in his teachers when he discovers that he has been given the "wrong information" in his high school course. The chemist, on the other hand, realizing that all descriptions of atoms take him beyond the level of concrete information, will not be surprised by such changes; he will expect them. This difference of outlook arises from the fact that the high school student was probably taught atomic *theory* as atomic *fact*.

By this point, it should be obvious that two scientists poring over the same set of data frequently devise two or more entirely different ways of relating them. From a common sense point of view, only one explanation of nature is "correct," but until all of the pertinent observations have been made, many tentatively "correct" answers are possible. (And since we can never make all of the relevant observations, this problem will always be with us.) Should new information not fit one of the existing interpretations, that pattern is discarded. Thus scientific theories come and go. As a matter of fact, subsequent data often prove that all interpretations are incorrect, thereby necessitating a completely new way of ordering the information at hand; the major "break-throughs" of science, such as the theory of evolution and the quantum theory, are the result.

Hence, as science progresses it tends to become more abstract and the more scientific information depends upon the scientist's interpretations, the more it is subject to change. Even more confusing for the layman is the fact that the interpretations made by scientists sometimes call for abstractions which give a "picture" represented by a series of mathematical equations impossible to visualize. In such cases the "model" obviously does not correspond to what one observes directly, but the scientist, lacking a better explanation, is willing to use it since it provides some of the order which he is seeking.

In science not only the *interpretation* of the "facts," but also the facts themselves will change as new techniques for obtaining measurements from nature are developed. As an example, until very recently the number of chromosomes in the human cell was firmly established at forty-eight, but a new technique, that of spreading the chromosomes for counting, determined that forty-six is a more accurate number and that even this figure is not constant.

In short, then, modern science consists of a rapidly increasing volume of information with an accompanying set of organizing principles (the theories of science), neither of which remains constant. Neither all the facts nor all the concepts of science which were "true" ten years ago can be accepted today.

The fact that information which is scientifically correct today may very well not be accurate when more data become available is even more frightening when seen from an educational point of view.

The three scientific subjects commonly taught in the high school (biology, chemistry, and physics) have, within the last hundred years, undergone the transition from the descriptive stage to the speculative stage. A major difficulty accompanying this frequently rapid change is that most high school textbooks still present these subjects as if no change had ever occurred. Most such books concentrate on the facts and to a lesser extent on the generalizations of science with little attention to the evidence upon which either are based. This approach leads to a rigid view of science, and it is therefore little wonder that the high school student often leaves his science courses with a distorted view of the nature of scientific knowledge.

The Nature of the Learner and of the Learning Process

Curriculum makers have traditionally maintained that motivation is a necessary prerequisite to effective learning. Such motivation has, for the most part, been attributed to the student's being able to see a relationship between what he studies in school and his everyday life. Thus science is frequently taught by showing its applicability to such things as driving an automobile, baking bread, and fishing. Unfortunately, this attempt to produce interest has had an undesirable side effect. In addition to augmenting the confusion described in the last section as to the nature of scientific fact and theory, this type of teaching has helped to produce a citizenry unable to distinguish between science, which is the discovering of knowledge, and technology, which is the application of scientific knowledge.

Recently the importance of another form of motivation for the learning of science has been vigorously advanced. This new motive might be described as "puzzle fascination." Almost everyone has observed it in hobbies such as solitaire, chess, crossword puzzles, and making collections of various sorts. The appeal of such diversions lies not in their practical value but in an inherent human interest in problematic situations and a natural desire to see a problem, once started, through to a solution. The proponents of puzzle fascination, as a source of motivation on which to base science teaching, argue strongly for instruction posed as a series of questions rather than as a series of answers. Disciples of this school of thought propose that any subject taught through questions which the student has a reasonable chance of answering will automatically be interesting to him.

This concept of motivation rejects the necessity of stressing the applicability of science to everyday life. Its defenders argue that puzzle fascination, being intrinsic, is a stronger motivating force than practical utility, which centers on things outside of the learner. Dedication to this point of view has led to the development of "discovery" teaching. In this approach, the student is placed on his own in a carefully contrived problematic situation and given just enough clues to enable him to have a reasonable chance of solving the problem. He is thus forced to "discover" major science generalizations for himself as opposed to having such information revealed to him by the teacher.

A second important psychological consideration involved in many of the newer approaches to science teaching is the idea of "massive general transfer." Many psychologists now believe that students can literally "learn how to learn." By being placed in problematic situations which force him to "discover" scientific generalizations, the student learns basic intellectual skills involved by inquiring into a problem whether science-related or not. According to this point of view, the student is made relationship-conscious; he gains skill in identifying relationships and begins to seek patterns in things he observes outside the classroom. The psychologists who support this position claim that this is the central purpose of all education.

Psychologists have also been giving considerable attention in recent years to the need for patterns in the subject matter being treated. Not long ago Jerome Bruner in his book *The Process of Education* made this startling statement: "We begin with the hypothesis that any subject can be taught effectively in some intellectually honest form to any child at any stage of development."[1] What Bruner is referring to is essentially the point of view used in developing the basic premises of programmed instruction. This amounts to saying that if one knows his subject matter well enough and can analyze it thoroughly, it is possible to take any idea, no matter how complex, and break it down into a series of very gradual steps which the learner can manage, and which will lead him unfailingly to the concept desired. According to Skinner and others, one can write a series of questions, each requiring very little knowledge beyond the preceding answer, that will lead the student to the mastery of virtually any concept.

It is obvious that if one subscribes to the psychological ideas presented here, the teaching of almost any science content can be justified, providing the method of approach is correct. It is also inherent in these ideas that the best approach to teaching any subject (particularly science) is through carefully phrased and sequenced questions built into the instructional materials used. This automatically means that the subject-matter specialist must be heavily involved in curriculum construction because he is the only one with sufficient insight into the content to phrase and sequence such questions.

The Nature of Modern American Society

In the early part of this century, the most important force in American society was technology. At that time the automobile, the radio, and the airplane were just coming into existence. Such innovations were modifying people's concepts of time, distance, and the good life. It was logical and necessary that the people should become acquainted with the technological advances behind the inventions

---

[1] Jerome S. Bruner, *The Process of Education* (Cambridge, Mass.: Harvard University Press, 1961), p. 33.

which were changing their lives. Technology, therefore, moved to the center of the high school science curricula.

We are now in a somewhat similar situation but the base is different. Technology is still proceeding at a fantastically rapid pace but many technological developments are applications of basic scientific ideas which were developed only five to ten years ago, whereas the principles of science which underlie the automobile, the radio, and the airplane go back fifty years or more. In addition, such developments are likely to be based on ideas of the sort discussed earlier, which are themselves tentative and subject to almost certain change. The time between the development of scientific theory and its application to practical situations has been drastically reduced; progress has now come to depend more upon the spawning of new ideas than upon ability to translate old ideas into new applications. In short, we are now living in a science-centered culture as opposed to the technology-centered one of only a few years ago.

This elevation of pure science to a position of vital cultural importance has brought with it serious problems. C. P. Snow put it well when he observed that we are gradually developing two cultures separated by an understanding of what science really is. Snow claims that the inability of the scientist and non-scientist to communicate poses the greatest problem for civilization.

This situation was well illustrated in a recent television program in which a United States senator and five scientists acted as a panel to discuss the role of government in the development of the scientific enterprise. At the beginning of the discussion the panel moderator asked the senator if he thought the federal government had been stimulating science sufficiently. The senator then went into a long explanation of why he felt that more public money should be invested in science. During his discourse he cited as examples the "small amounts of money" which had been spent on space exploration, atomic bombs, new aircraft, and similar projects.

The camera then passed to one of the scientists on the panel who said, "I am afraid that I cannot agree with you, Senator."

The disturbed senator wanted to know if the scientist thought the government was spending too much money on science. "No, Senator, the government has spent almost nothing on science," the scientist replied, dumbfounding the senator. "The millions of dollars about which you were just talking have very little to do with science."

At this point the program developed into a one-way discussion with the five scientists speaking with a single voice in trying to explain to the senator just what science is. The basis of the conversation involved, of course, the distinction between pure scientific research aimed at the discovery of knowledge which better explains the facts at hand, and technology (the senator's conception of science) aimed at finding new applications of scientific principles.

The lesson here is clear. It is this senator who will vote on bills which may determine the amount of pure research to be done, and, therefore, the number of new ideas in science which will be generated in the United States. From his comments, one might conclude that the senator's vote will probably hinge on the question, "What results will this research bring?" Unfortunately, pure research cannot be evaluated on the basis of practical applications.

This confusion of science with technology—this complete misunderstanding of the nature and aims of modern science—could well be disastrous for the United States. The problem is not restricted to high government officials; unfortunately, the average citizen has a conception of science very much akin to the senator's, and it is he who will elect future senators. It appears that though we now have a science-centered culture, many of our citizens do not understand the nature of its dominant force. The clear dangers of this situation require no elaboration.

Implications for Science Curriculum

The factors so far discussed are those that have influenced the recent developments in secondary school science instruction. Considerations of this sort motivated the groups that developed the new courses in physics, biology, and chemistry to be described in the following chapters. Now individual authors are using these ideas in developing other courses which they hope will further improve science education.

Although the new courses deal with quite diverse kinds of science, a great deal of similarity is involved. In the first place, all the courses tend to deal with relatively "pure" science; there is less concern for relating science principles to everyday life. This view, stemming from the notion that the student should be able to cope with a wider variety of everyday life situations, by learning more basic science principles, does not imply that applied science is unimportant. This approach is considered more economical because any course based on applied science must necessarily include an incalculable volume of varied examples, since it is impossible to predict the situations a given student is likely to encounter after he leaves school, and must run the risk of new technological developments outdating whatever examples may be selected.

In addition, all of the newer courses tend to emphasize a laboratory approach to science. They attempt to use the laboratory as a means of discovering science, not, as is frequently the case, as a verification of what is presented in the textbook. All the new curricula encourage the student to behave like a scientist in the solution of problems. Through this procedure, it is hoped that motivation will be increased and the student will learn something of the process by which scientific information is unearthed. This concentration on the nature of scientific inquiry is considered particularly important in countering the confusion as to the aims and methods of the scientist, described in an earlier section.

The ideas incorporated into the laboratory work of the new programs are extended by including in the text frequent references to how a particular concept was arrived at. The textbooks include numerous descriptions of experiments done by famous scientists and references to the methods used to bring forth the more important generalizations.

To summarize then, the developers of the new curricula have attempted to cause the student to discover for himself major science generalizations. The authors have chosen to ignore the fact that this approach leaves large gaps in the amount of scientific knowledge which a given student acquires. It is assumed that a science cannot be "covered" in one semester, but the student provided with certain basic intellectual tools for attacking problems and with the basic scientific generalizations which underlie most of technology is likely to be able to adapt to a variety of situations. Further, it is hoped that the student will become scientifically literate in that he will have a better understanding of how and why scientists approach problems, and will therefore be less likely to be guilty of the kind of science ignorance which is so widespread today.

In the next three chapters the ideas presented here will be extended through an analysis of the sciences of physics, biology, and chemistry. In addition, we will look carefully at the ways in which specific new approaches to teaching these subjects are organized.

CHAPTER II

The Transformation of High School Physics—A Case Study

In the previous chapter, the point was made that the science we teach in the schools must resemble science itself. The revolution in the discovery of new knowledge in physics has been no less striking than that in any other branch of science, and the implications of this fact are clear. Physics taught in the decade of the sixties in the same way that it was taught ten years earlier is inherently not good physics. The methods and procedures of physics teachers must reflect a change of the same magnitude as the change in physics content.

Of the important changes in secondary school science curriculum and teaching methods that have taken place since 1956, the innovations in physics should be examined with particular care for a special reason. It was in physics that the first curriculum-reform efforts in science were made and the first of the new curriculum programs was completed and released to the schools. For this reason we will examine the early history of the most important new physics curriculum development and note its progress with particular interest. The curriculum programs in biology and chemistry, which were developed between 1958 and 1964, have followed generally similar patterns.

A New Physics for High Schools

With the increased interest in physics that resulted from the technological explosion during and after World War II, and with the more important role of science in the affairs of men, the need to examine the nature of high school physics instruction became more urgent. Following World War II various individuals and groups became concerned with the quality of the high school course and began to initiate change. The most important and far-reaching of these efforts was the new program in high school physics developed

11

by the Physical Science Study Committee, which began operation in 1956 under a grant from the National Science Foundation. Between 1956 and 1960 the Physical Science Study Committee (PSSC) group, with the assistance of well over one hundred college and university physicists, professional educators, high school science teachers, industrial physicists, film production experts, and other technical people carried out what may very well be the most ambitious program of curriculum revision in the history of American education. The PSSC group produced an entirely new course. The Committee has overseen the production of a textbook, a completely new laboratory program, a teacher's guide, a complete set of instructional films, and a large collection of semi-popular monographs designed for out-of-class reading. As the first of the major efforts to remake high school science in America—and as one of the most far-reaching—the PSSC course, especially its historical past, deserves examination.

The general dissatisfaction among university physicists with the state of secondary school physics teaching provided the impetus for a series of informal meetings in 1956. These discussions were stimulated primarily by Dr. Jerrold Zacharias, professor of physics at the Massachusetts Institute of Technology. At about the same time, efforts by the American Institute of Physics, the American Association of Physics Teachers, and the National Science Teachers Association were also underway. The complaints against the physics courses being taught in most American high schools were the following:

1. Textbooks in general reflected a scientific outlook that dated back half a century and was no longer representative of the views of the scientific community.

2. Genuine attempts to remain abreast of scientific developments had given even the best textbooks a patchwork quality in which the unity of physics disappeared.

3. The sheer mass of material in the textbooks had become so great that it could no longer be reasonably taught in an academic year or even in two years.

4. With the increasing application of science to the everyday environment, physics textbooks had given more and more attention to technology and less and less to the concepts of science, thus further overloading the course and minimizing its unity.[1]

---

[1] Physical Science Study Committee, *Physics,* First Annual Report I, Preliminary Edition, 3.

The first major task facing the Committee was the determination of a course of study. The first meeting which was called for the purpose of examining the philosophies of the members of the Committee revealed a number of important differences with respect to what should be taught in high school physics, but it revealed also the existence of a common purpose and, to a considerable degree, a common philosophy of education in physics. Some consideration was given at this point to undertaking the building of a combined physics-chemistry course which would cover a two-year period. In the end it was decided that the long-range purposes of PSSC might involve the preparation of such an integrated course but that as a practical matter it would be more expedient to produce first a one-year course in physics with the inclusion of certain important ideas from the field of chemistry.

The following statement gives the thinking which guided the development of the syllabus:

> The criteria were many, and in order to justify inclusion any given subject matter had to meet them all. To begin with, it was desired that the course stress the major achievements of physics: the great, penetrating conceptions such as the conservation principles. Next, it was desired that the course give the student insight into the manner in which these powerful ideas were born, matured, and (in some cases) superseded by even more powerful ideas.
>
> The entire story was to be a unified story, in which the interconnections of all physics were brought to light. Finally, all this was to be presented as a human activity, set within society and carried on as part of the historical development of mankind.[2]

During the summer of 1957, a large group of physicists and high school teachers set about the production of a preliminary version of the textbook. Sections of this first volume were supplied to the schools in August of that year so that a period of testing of the new course could begin with the opening of school in September.

The production of suitable films to accompany the text and laboratory portion of the program has been a major goal of the Committee since the beginning. As with the textbook, the Committee conducted an extensive study of films already in use and after many hours of inspecting available films, the PSSC Film Program began to take shape. It is anticipated that some seventy-five films will ultimately be produced as part of the PSSC program.

---

[2] *Ibid.*, p. 4.

The third major component of the PSSC course is the laboratory program. The criteria established by the Committee for each experiment are as follows:

> 1. Experiments should indeed be experiments, and not the routine accumulation of data to agree with (or be forced into agreement with) a result known well in advance by both teacher and student.
> 2. Experiments should be performed wherever possible with simple apparatus that could be made by the students from inexpensive materials.
> 3. The laboratory work should be open-ended in that each experiment should suggest and encourage further experiments along similar lines, and wherever possible lead to the consideration of theoretical ideas flowing from experiments.

> The essential purpose of the laboratory work is to contribute to the understanding of the course as a whole. It is not intended to teach special techniques for their own sake, nor to explore the technological applications of scientific principles.
> Experiments are to be intimately related to the text. Thus, measurements are made which are either the basis of discussion in the text, or which solve problems raised by the text. In the laboratory, the student employs the methods used to measure the distance to the nearest star and the dimensions of the molecule. From such personal activity, he derives a feeling for magnitudes that no amount of reading or discussion could bring him; moreover, he learns measurement as part of the process of doing physics, rather than as a disjointed special topic.[3]

Early in the program serious thought was given to having students build as much of their own laboratory apparatus as possible. The feeling was that not only would such an effort make apparatus available at lower cost to the schools but it would also guarantee certain desirable learning outcomes. The plans have changed considerably in this regard and it has now been decided that overall efficiency in the course will be increased by having the materials produced by commercial science supply houses. The laboratory apparatus is still for the most part relatively inexpensive and durable and makes use of such simple equipment as can be produced in the school or at home if an enterprising physics teacher wishes to do it that way.

The monographs have been designed to fill a special need among both teachers and students for supplementary reading material in physics. One important reason for producing such a set of books

[3] *Ibid.*, p. 8.

was to provide material covering the traditional subject matter which had been omitted from the PSSC course, but which is nevertheless important in the science of physics. At the same time it was believed that a collection of sound and readable science books would appeal to readers outside the high school physics course. They might reach other high school students, college students, and a large segment of the reading public.

The Committee has prepared for those teaching the PSSC course an extensive collection of teaching aids in the form of a teacher's guide. In addition to answering the textbook questions and problems, the teacher's guide offers suggestions as to how the textbook materials should be handled from the point of view of teachers with varied backgrounds and experiences. A running commentary on the textbook is included, giving the purpose, content, and emphasis of each part of the text and including considerable background information. Recommendations for homework assignments are made. In addition, each laboratory experiment is discussed and special hints are provided on such things as how the experiment should articulate with the text materials along with background information and comments on the timing and relative importance of the experiments. Questions that appear in the students' laboratory guide are discussed.

Between 1956 and 1960, the PSSC course was tried in scores of schools under the direction of hundreds of teachers. The tryout was carefully controlled and observed by members of the PSSC group. Special pains were taken to insure that those who would teach the course had developed some understanding of its philosophy and some knowledge of the special pedagogical methods necessary for the teacher to demonstrate this philosophy in his classroom and laboratory. Special summer and in-service institutes, generally supported by the National Science Foundation, were held for this purpose in dozens of colleges and universities throughout the country.

In 1960, with the appearance of a hardback edition of the textbook (which was produced by a commercial publisher),* the PSSC course was made available to all schools. It is now the basic course for nearly half the students who are studying physics in American high schools, and in addition is widely used in Great Britain and other countries.

The PSSC course is important for its own sake and also as a pat-

---

* Physical Science Study Committee, *Physics* (Boston: D. C. Heath & Company), 1960.

tern for curriculum development. Here, for the first time in the history of American education, we have seen a close working relationship between the scientific scholars and the professional educators, including professors of education, high school teachers, and other specialists. Here, too, for the first time, we have observed the production of a high school course by a large number of expert scientists, many of whom had not until this time given serious thought to science education at the secondary school level. And here for the first time in science curriculum development was an admission by responsible scientists and educators that all of the important topics in a particular field could not be taught in the basic course in high school, and that certain arbitrary selections of topics would have to be made. This would enable the topics included to be taught in some depth so that the students could be given a real taste of science and could develop some understanding of the methods by which scientists approach problems in their laboratories.

The Historical Basis of Modern Physics Teaching

Of all the sciences, physics—especially modern physics—is perhaps most difficult to understand without some understanding of its history, of the contributions of the early physicists, and of the order in which their contributions were made.

For present purposes one might well begin the history of physics with Nicolas Copernicus who was born in 1473. The life of Copernicus touched on many things including medicine, finance, politics, and religion, but his greatest contribution was his new world system which placed the sun in the center of the universe. His substantial arguments in support of this notion provided the simplest and the best answer to the age-old problem which had troubled Greek astronomers and philosophers—how to explain the apparent movements of the heavens in terms of uniform circular motions. He proposed that all bodies possess gravity. Following Copernicus, the apparent motions of the heavenly bodies were explained by Kepler and Tycho Brahe, the Danish nobleman whose observations were the most accurate in scientific work up to that time.

In the Sixteenth Century William Gilbert and Francis Bacon contributed to the establishment of the "scientific method." Bacon's approach to the problems of science was essentially experimental relying largely on the inductive method on which scientific investigation rests so heavily today.

Galileo, who lived from 1564 to 1642, carried out important research in mechanics and astronomy. He, too, was interested in the "systems of the world" and in the rival theories of Ptolemy and Copernicus. He investigated the optical properties of glass, became interested in "perspective glasses" which would magnify distant objects, and built a highly effective telescope. It was Galileo who did much to encourage the intellectual revolution which was inaugurated by Copernicus.

Isaac Newton was born in 1642, the year in which Galileo died. The laws of Newton, including his law of universal gravitation, stand as monuments to his work today. At the age of twenty-two he invented the differential calculus, and by twenty-three the integral calculus. His penetrations into the nature of matter left us a wealth of knowledge.

Anything approaching a complete account of the contributions of the physical scientists in this era is quite impossible here. The rapid scientific progress of the period is difficult to measure exactly, but most historians would probably agree with Sir James Jeans who referred to the Seventeenth Century as the Century of Genius.

Meanwhile the first serious contributions to the fund of knowledge of the physical sciences in America were being made. The first notable scientific society was founded by Benjamin Franklin at Philadelphia in 1743. Franklin was, no doubt, one of the top men of science whom America has produced. While acclaiming his role in securing independence for the colonies we should not fail to recognize that his famous kite experiment provided the first real knowledge of the nature of electricity and attests to his zeal as an experimenter.

Toward the end of the Nineteenth Century a new era of scientific progress was ushered in. Samuel Langley began to investigate the principles of flight and his work contributed heavily to the later success of the Wright brothers. The American physicist Michelson accurately measured the speed of light, thereby strengthening certain convictions which were soon to result in Einstein's celebrated relativity theory. Thomas Edison was pushing the boundaries of science and technology forward by leaps and bounds at his laboratory at Menlo Park. The Curies had discovered radium, J. J. Thomson the electron, and Lord Rutherford had identified alpha rays and beta particles. An obscure German physics teacher discovered X-rays and by so doing threw panic into the hearts of a generation of modest females who feared the worst. E. O. Lawrence designed and built the first cyclotron to accelerate particles for use in nuclear experiments and Hurtz gave us radio waves.

In the Twentieth Century the physicists were to probe the atom and to harness the incalculable energy released from nuclear fission and nuclear fusion. The two world wars served to hasten progress in science. In the period since 1945 the expansion of knowledge in physical science has continued to accelerate as new discoveries are made at a fantastic rate.

This short history of physics provides some insight into the nature of physics and the means by which progress in this branch of science has been made. Even the casual student of the history of science will observe that progress came when men began to make careful observations of natural phenomena, of the objects and events in the physical world around them. The difference between Galileo and Aristotle, for example, can be most easily seen in a comparison of their views of natural phenomena. Aristotle subscribed to the notion that natural events are a part of a "grand scheme" and therefore attempts to conduct experiments and to make careful, precise observations of natural events serve no useful end; man's efforts ought rather to be directed toward a philosophical understanding of things. Galileo, on the other hand, was first and foremost an experimenter and if a theory did not stand up under careful observation, if it could not be supported by experimental evidence, he did not accept it as scientific fact—though he might have laid it aside for only a brief period, to examine it again later under different circumstances.

But if a review of the history of physics tells us that early science was rooted in observation and experiment, it also helps to explain why, as stated earlier, people have tended to view scientists as describers of nature and science as an accumulation of their observations. Not until well into the Twentieth Century was physics regarded as something which students might explore, as an area where youngsters could flex their intellectual muscles. In the past, physics has generally been looked upon as a study in which one commits to memory the theories and laws contributed by the observers and the experimenters, but rarely, if ever, becomes involved in the observation and experimentation himself. Students of physics have traditionally devoted themselves to a study of the work of Galileo, Newton, Rutherford, and Einstein in a manner calculated to encourage the memorization of information and to discourage independent investigation in their classrooms and laboratories.

If the teaching of modern physics is to succeed, students must somehow be helped to understand that independent thought and exploration in the formulation of hypotheses are necessary, that it is not enough to commit to memory the information left by earlier experimenters and to go into the laboratory only for the purpose of confirming the experimental evidence already memorized. The present age demands a different approach to the teaching of physics, but the history of physics provides little help in finding this approach. The manner in which the student views the science he studies must surely influence his views of the science. If we expect people to regard science as an honest effort to unravel the mysteries of the natural world, high school science must be taught as an open-ended activity in which the student is encouraged to go beyond the information obtained, to realize that questions are often as important as answers, and to recognize the transition of science from the descriptive to the speculative. By such means will the scientifically literate citizen be better able to cope with the great variety of problem situations which arise out of the dominance of science in today's world.

The Evolution of High School Physics in America

When the first public high school in this country was opened in Boston in 1821, physics was included in its curriculum. The education law of Massachusetts in 1857 required all public high schools to give courses in "natural philosophy." The growth of laboratory work came slowly but in the latter part of the Nineteenth Century laboratory work came to be emphasized. The quantitative approach, with heavy stress on mathematics, was much in evidence although the quality of both textbooks and laboratory experiments was poor.

In 1886 the *Harvard Descriptive List of Experiments* required for admission to most colleges was published. This was a list of forty experiments which Harvard College established as prerequisites to admission. Shortly after 1900 the course was reorganized with increased emphasis on those aspects of the science which had some usefulness to the students. Teachers sought material which would relate the course to the needs of the learner rather than to the structure of physics itself. High school physics changed relatively little from about 1915 to 1950 despite a number of important advances in the science. In physics, as in the other sciences, the gap between the discovery of scientific knowledge and its introduction into the classroom had grown much too wide.

High school physics has been taken almost exclusively by college bound students. The percent of high school students taking physics has declined disturbingly in the period 1880–1960. While the actual enrollment figures are more comforting—there were 100,000 students studying the course in 1890 and about 400,000 in 1960—the failure of more students to take physics in high school has been a matter of concern to educators and scientists. During the early part of the century a high percentage of high school students had small expectation of attending college; most of those youngsters therefore declined to study physics since it was considered to have almost solely a college entrance function. But it is worth noting that a recent survey of high school graduates in Maryland disclosed that a surprisingly high percentage of the better students take physics—of those in the "academically talented" category (IQ above 120) seventy-nine percent of the boys and thirty-eight percent of the girls had taken the course in high school.[4] The percentage of bright students who study physics throughout the nation is probably well above fifty percent.

The Traditional High School Physics Course

As a means of comparing the old with the new, let us examine in some detail a traditional high school physics course—the kind used in most American high schools until recently and still used in many. The textbook used for such a course may be divided into eight or ten units with perhaps three or four chapters per unit. The first unit very likely introduces the science of physics by defining a number of terms such as energy, matter, and the several properties of matter.

---

4 Orval L. Ulry, "A Study of the Relationship Between Subjects Taken and Other Selected Factors for the Class of 1958, Maryland Public High Schools," *The Science Teacher,* Vol. XXVII, No. 5 (September, 1960), 23.

The conservation of energy may well be presented early in the course, along with the concept of matter as composed of molecules and atoms, with some attention being given to the behavior of molecules.

The second unit may very well deal with the behavior of fluids. Here the student would consider force and pressure in liquids and gases, buoyancy, specific gravity and density, the atmosphere and its pressure, with some attention probably being given to the physics of lighter-than-air aircraft (why they stay aloft), and transportation in and on the water. He begins at about this point to work mathematical problems involving force and pressure and the laboratory work may include experiments and demonstrations involving air pressure and the barometer, water pressure, and the determination of the specific gravity of liquids.

A study of work, energy, and machines may follow. The student attempts to develop an understanding of energy and work. He analyzes forces and learns to find a resultant of two or more forces acting together. He may give considerable attention to calculating mechanical advantage and efficiency in various simple machines; also to friction between their working parts. In this section, Newton's laws of motion are typically taken up as the student undertakes a study of velocity and acceleration. Applications are made to commonplace objects, including automobiles, trains, airplanes, rockets, and other familiar devices. Excellent opportunities exist for emphasizing the important role which mathematics plays in the study of physics—for example, in making calculations involving the velocity, altitude, and time to reach the earth of a bomb dropped from an airplane.

The unit on heat, which often follows that on mechanics, typically provides a historical account of the work of Count Rumford and other early physicists who worked in this field. The distinction between heat and temperature is made and the science of thermometry is introduced. The definition of the calorie, the unit for measuring heat, is given and the notion of specific heat of bodies is explained with the student generally being required to calculate the quantity of heat exchanged when warm and cold substances are mixed. The effect of heat on the expansion of various materials is taken up along with the transfer of heat by convection, conduction, and radiation. The physics of the weather may be introduced in this section along with heat of fusion and vaporization, condensation, humidity, high and low pressure zones, and related topics. Heat engines—the steam engine, steam turbine, diesel engine, and the internal combustion engine—are often given some attention. In recent textbooks rocket engines are also studied.

In the unit on sound, the student's attention may be directed first to the matter of sound transmission by waves. Longitudinal and transverse waves are analyzed and the various characteristics of sounds considered. Mathematical problems involving the speed, wave length, and frequency of sound waves are typical.

The unit on light generally devotes some attention to the various theories of light energy. Some attention is given to reflection from plane surfaces (mirrors) and then to concave and convex surfaces. The student learns to construct images produced by mirrors and through these comes to understand the behavior of reflected light. Next he studies refraction, the bending of light rays as they pass from one medium to another. He may then analyze various kinds of lenses and consider their use in optical instruments such as the sextant, the microscope, the telescope, and eye glasses. Again he attacks problems involving frequency, wave length, and speed of light and gives some attention to color and pigments.

The student generally begins the unit on magnetism and electricity with the study of natural magnets and continues with a working theory of magnetism. This is followed by a study of magnetic induction and the magnetic field of the earth. At this point static electricity may be introduced. The electroscope is used to demonstrate charging by induction and to identify an unknown charge on a charged body. The nature of electro-magnetism and its uses in industry and science are emphasized. Ohm's Law showing how the volt, the ampere, and the ohm relate to one another is introduced and in most courses is given a good deal of time and attention. The production of electricity both by chemical means and by electro-magnetic induction is described. The production of heat and light from electricity is considered with applications to irons, heaters, lamps and similar devices. Chemical effects of electric currents including electrolysis and electroplating, the chemical action of storage cells and other type of electric cells, alternating current and its generation, with attention to various kinds of commercial generators, rectifiers, and other industrial machines—are all studied in the chapter on electricity and magnetism.

There may be a separate unit on electronics or it may be taken up as part of the previous unit. Here the student studies the vacuum tube, X-rays, transistors, the cathode ray oscilloscope, and the electron microscope, thus giving his major attention to the technical aspects of electronics. Radar likely comes in for some attention along with the equipment used in television transmission and reception.

At about this point in the course some of the more popular books include a unit on transportation where special attention is given to the mechanical operation of the automobile, the airplane, and more recently, perhaps the rocket. The forces and mechanics involved in the takeoff, the control in flight, and the landing of the aircraft may be studied. In the final unit, which might very well be called modern physics, the student would likely be introduced to radioactivity and to a more detailed study of the nucleus of the atom. He would then learn the meaning of radioactive decay and would study such machines as particle accelerators and atomic reactors. Some attention would likely be given to radio isotopes and atomic fission and fusion, both in bombs and under control for the production of useful power.

The high school physics course just described is typical of the physics presently given in the majority of the nation's high schools. Though it has been designed for the student who will go on to college, it emphasizes the applications of physics to industrial machines of many kinds. It attempts to give coverage to nearly all aspects of physics. Recent topics are included mostly near the end of the course and few, if any, of the earlier topics have been deleted. The course has no particular unifying theme, but begins with the customary introduction to physics and then proceeds from the study of mechanics, with which the student is perhaps most familiar, to sound, then to light, then to electrical phenomena, and finally to modern physics, with which he is apt to be less familiar. Its heavy emphasis on various kinds of machines and electrical equipment probably leaves the girls in the class at some disadvantage and this may be, as some have claimed, a major reason for the small number of girls who typically take physics in high school.

The foregoing course does have considerable material of immediate personal interest to students. On the basis of his study of electricity, for example, the student should be able to calculate the cost of operating a particular electrical appliance for a given period of time, and he should be able to understand the operation of such devices as the microscope, most musical instruments, submarines, and a large number of machines of the pulley, wheel-and-axle, and lever type. In addition, he will have had contact with most of the topics covered in physics at the college level and may, therefore, be prompted to undertake further study on his own. The teacher is, of course, often free to delete certain topics and give further emphasis to others if he desires. And he may organize his course around local problems or interests. It is possible for the teacher using a subject matter outline similar to the one described here to develop his course following a variety of approaches (for example, "environmental physics"), provided the class has access to certain supplementary reading materials and a good array of laboratory equipment. If the teacher chooses to build a course stressing certain of the large underlying principles of physics, and to follow these as continuous threads through the course, he will very likely have to depart from the course described above in many important ways and rely heavily upon supplementary reading materials.

But to those who see the need for a different kind of physics for high school students, the most serious flaw in this course is that it has no theoretical base—or, at best, a very weak one. There is little to tie the various topics together. The relationship of light waves to radio waves, for example, is scarcely noticed; yet this "oneness" of the whole electromagnetic spectrum is one of the fundamental ideas in physics. Likewise, the student's attention early in the course is not really directed to understanding the role of certain important concepts in the later nuclear physics section. This absence of a unifying theme, of any real attempt to show the unity and the order of the science, lays the traditional physics course open to its most serious criticism.

The PSSC Physics Course

In contrast with the traditional physics course described above, the PSSC course has four major sections entitled: *The Universe, Optics and Waves, Mechanics,* and *Electricity and Atomic Structure.*

In Part One of the book, *The Universe,* the student is concerned with man's fundamental notions of the world, with matter in the dimensions of space and time. He deals with time in microseconds and in billions of years, and in order to describe these great ranges of time, orders of magnitude are introduced. From here his attention is directed to the measurement of both small and large distances. The student learns that man must resort to certain devices to extend his senses in measuring things that are too small or too large for his eye to handle, and he uses significant figures to express the reliability of his measurements.

The topic of motion is then taken up with the student's attention first being directed to motion along a straight line. He learns to use a graph to relate speed and time and he is shown that speed is the slope of a distance-time graph. Acceleration is seen to be derived from the slope of a velocity-time graph. The study of motion along a line is extended to motion in space with the introduction of vectors.

Mass and matter—and the distinction between them is stressed—are then considered. At this point, Part One of the course begins to look somewhat like a high school chemistry course for it takes up atomic structure, the laws of chemical composition, atomic mass units, and the natural units out of which matter is built, the proton and the electron. The arrangement of atoms in solids and gases is discussed and this leads to the idea of building a model to explain what one observes.

Early in Part Two of the PSSC course, *Optics and Waves,* the student is encouraged to build a mental model* for the behavior of light, after dealing with the laws of reflection and refraction. He is encouraged to consider light as being made up of small particles. When he takes this model to the laboratory and subjects it to experiment, he finds that it just doesn't work. He is then led to examine another model, this time one which attempts to explain the behavior of light in terms of waves. In the end the student comes to understand that neither the particle model nor the wave model is sufficient to explain all that he observes in his study of light, but that each helps to explain certain things, and that the two together help him understand the behavior of light.

In Part Two of the course, the relationship between the laboratory and the textbook is particularly close. In addition to showing the particle model to be inadequate, the student's laboratory work involves ropes and springs for the study of transmission of energy by pulses; the study of the behavior of waves in a ripple tank, a shallow tray

---

* A mental model may be described as a picture, or model, which exists only in the mind, of certain phenomena or structures which cannot be perceived by use of the senses.

with a glass bottom, is undertaken. By this means diffraction and interference of light waves are analyzed.

This section also gives attention to a good many of the topics taken up in the traditional physics course: the construction of images formed by mirrors and lenses, index of refraction, and Snell's law. But its deep concern with such notions as the pressure exerted by a beam of light and the wave nature of light should convince the student that the study of light must go beyond the descriptive level; it must be analytic in keeping with the open-ended nature of investigation in physics.

In a sense, Part III follows Part I; but whereas Part One was concerned mostly with kenematics, Part Three, *Mechanics,* is concerned with dynamics—with motion and the relation between force and motion. The student is directed to the experiments of Galileo; his laboratory experiments lead him to a determination of the relation between velocity, force, acceleration, and mass—in other words, to Newton's law. In this section there is considerable emphasis on man's attempt to build models from his observations of the solar system, on the history of physical thought beginning with the speculations of the early Greeks and continuing through Copernicus, Brahe, Kepler, and Newton.

Energy and work are introduced in this section of the book and the elastic collision between masses is analyzed as an illustration of the conservation of energy. The exchange between the two forms of energy, kinetic and potential, is examined, and finally, the notion of the conservation of energy is extended to include thermal energy.

Part Four, entitled *Electricity and Modern Physics,* in a sense completes the circle for it returns to the atomic nature of matter which was introduced in Part One. The student is now able to look quantitatively at atomic structure; through the use of the wave properties which he studied in Part Two of the textbook and the particle mechanics in Part Three, he is able to form a wave-mechanical description of the behavior of matter which is required for an understanding of the behavior of atoms. Electricity is viewed as one of the natural characteristics of matter, the atomic glue which binds the parts of an atom together; electricity is introduced but Ohm's law, which makes up the heart of most traditional physics courses, is hardly noticed here.

Electrical potential difference is studied and a method for measuring the paths of the proton and the electron is shown.

One of the important ideas in this section is the establishment of the notion of the particle nature of electric charge. This is accomplished through a thorough textbook description coupled with the presentation on film of a modified Millikan oil-drop experiment. It is then possible to establish the force constant in Coulomb's law (which establishes the relationship between charge and distance in electric forces) and to compare electrical and gravitational forces.

From here the student's attention is directed to the use of the mass spectrograph to measure the mass of charged particles; to the electromagnetic spectrum and the suggestion that energy is being transmitted by waves; and finally to the possibility of matter waves and a quantum mechanical picture of the structure of matter. Part Four serves to bring together the first three parts of the book in the student's analysis of electricity and modern physics.[5]

In comparing the PSSC course with more traditional high school physics courses one is tempted to sum up the most readily apparent differences by stating that the former emphasizes the development of principles and understandings of basic physical relations, while the latter stresses technological applications and memorization of formulas. While this may be an oversimplification it is not without meaning. There is considerable difference of opinion as to the appropriateness of the PSSC course for those students who typically take high school physics in this country, largely because it is often considered too "theoretical" for the average physics student. The arguments over this question will not be laid to rest easily or soon and there may be no simple answer.

As a group, the physicists in the United States seem to have endorsed the PSSC course enthusiastically, a fact which ought to have some meaning in determining what physics should be taught to our youngsters. Whether or not the PSSC course eventually will be adopted by most American high schools in its present form is not the most important issue. There is no denying that the PSSC program has already had a profound influence on physics instruction in this country and this influence will assuredly continue and probably increase in the years ahead. Though the question of whether the PSSC course is better or worse than traditional physics will likely never be

---

[5] The description of the PSSC course given here is based largely on: "Secondary School Physics: The Physical Science Study Committee," *Review of the Secondary School Physics Program of the Physical Science Study Committee* (Watertown, Mass.: Educational Services Inc., 1959), pp. 37–42.

settled to the satisfaction of all science teachers and educators, it would be difficult to deny that the following characteristics of the PSSC course stand out in any comparison of PSSC and traditional physics:

1. The course covers less topical material than is usually presented in high school physics while penetrating more deeply into selected areas which contribute most heavily to an understanding of the universe.

2. Physical models are developed and used as they are by scientists in attempting to explain phenomena.

3. Physics is treated as a unified, interconnected story, and as a human activity "set within our society and carried on as part of the historical development of mankind."

4. Less emphasis is placed on technological applications of physics and more on an understanding of fundamental principles.

5. The laboratory is integrated more closely with the rest of the course than is customary.

6. The materials provided for the student and the teacher—textbook, Laboratory Guide, Teacher's Guide, films, and monographs—make a more complete kit of materials for learning than have been available in any course previously.

Problems that Remain

The study of physics in our high schools is undergoing serious ferment. Thoughtful educators are addressing themselves to a large number of problems; they include the question of whether high school physics, at least for the less capable students, should be largely theoretical or whether it should be directed toward problems of engineering and technology; the identification and description of the "average" physics student; the disturbingly low enrollment figures for high school physics; the proper education of high school physics teachers; the proper grade placement of physics in the high school science sequence; the possible development of a two-year coordinated physics-chemistry course to replace the two courses now offered separately in most high schools; and the articulation of high school physics with the physics that is studied—or should be studied—in the lower grades and at the college level. These questions will be discussed in Chapter VII in the broad context of the high school science program.

CHAPTER III

The New Biology — And New Ways
to Teach It

Earlier chapters have emphasized that we must somehow enable students in high school to see that their courses in science are really a part of the total fabric of science, that science for students must correspond to science as it is practiced and understood by scientists. It was specifically suggested that students of modern science in high school should be made aware of the "basics" of science which are least likely to change with time—the nature of the processes by which scientific information is unearthed and, perhaps more importantly, the tentative nature of scientific knowledge.

As has been shown in Chapter II, all of this has great implication for the teaching of physics, where the subject matter consists largely of abstract concepts like atoms, energy, force, and mass. But how can biology be understood in these terms? Here the scientist deals with concrete things like dogs, frogs, trees, and birds. Isn't biology simply having the student do what biologists do: namely, observe plants and animals carefully (perhaps slice them open in the process), describe them minutely (perhaps draw or photograph them), and attach names (mostly in Latin) to the result? Doesn't studying biology really boil down to learning the names of organisms, groups of organisms, or parts of organisms—and, in some cases, to considering certain applications of these things to health and conservation?

The answer to these questions from a present-day point of view is an unequivocal No! During the early years of biological science, before the discrete bits of information about living things had begun to be gathered into major theories or concepts (mental models), such an approach might have been defensible. Those days are, however, long past. Biological research (particularly that done in the past ten years) has begun to approach that of the physical sciences in the development of unifying bodies of theory. The themes arising from this research plus the skills in inquiry which led to them are only now beginning to be reflected in high school biology teaching. The relative newness of these developments means that the teaching of biological science is the science area perhaps *most* in need of modernizing in terms of the ideas discussed in Chapter I.

The Nature of Modern Biological Science

Perhaps the major difference between biology as it is practiced and biology as it is conceived of by most laymen and represented in many high school courses lies in the fact that the biologist of today operates on the assumption that the basic processes occurring in living things are no different from those which are present in non-living matter. This means that, though the reactions are much more complex and highly interrelated, the determination of just how the atoms and molecules which make up living things react with one another and with those that make up the environment to produce what we call life becomes one of the most important problems in biological science. As a matter of fact, life is sometimes defined in terms of the kinds of chemical and physical reactions which go on in living things. This means that the biologist of today finds himself dealing more and more with problems that are basically mathematical, chemical, and physical.

That biological science would move in this direction was completely predictable at least thirty years ago. By that time the philosophical foundations had been laid down. What remained was for the chemists, physicists, and mathematicians to advance their sciences to the point where they could be used as tools for dealing with the very complex phenomena occurring in living things. In addition, the biologist himself had to become well enough acquainted with chemistry, physics, and mathematics to use them effectively as tools (or, alternatively, chemists, physicists, and mathematicians had to become interested in the challenging problems to be found in biology). These difficulties have only begun to be resolved in the last ten to fifteen years and this development, perhaps more than any other, has led to the great conceptual advances which characterize modern biology.

The import of the changes which have occurred in biology can probably best be appreciated through an example. The historical development of the concept of the "gene" illustrates rather well the

changes in basic approach, the shift from description to conceptuali-
zation, the heavy dependence on other sciences, and the sort of
thought which is prevalent in biology today.

About the time of the American Civil War an Austrian monk,
Gregor Mendel, carried on a number of very interesting experiments
with plants. He grew large numbers of common pea plants and noted
certain observable differences between them in such characteristics
as seed shape, seed sugar content, flower color, and leaf shape. He
kept careful notes on the distribution of these traits among plants
which were bred together. He then planted the seeds from these par-
ents, and studied the characteristics of the offspring. His basic purpose was to search for a relationship between the appearance of the
parent plants and that of their offspring.

After several hundred such crosses, a pattern began to emerge.
Mendel noted that if he *assumed* that the appearance of the traits
which he observed was under the control of something which he
called "factors" and that these factors operated in special ways, he
could successfully *predict* the characteristics of the offspring of any
two plants crossed.

It should be noted here that Mendel never saw any of his factors
and that his reasoning was of the "if-then" variety. In essence he
said, *"If* I assume these things to be true, *then* I can predict what I
see." The fact that he could make predictions on the basis of his
postulates did not mean that they were necessarily true but rather
that they represented *one* way of explaining what had been seen. In
other words, Mendel built a model which accounted for his observations.

Mendel published his results and to a great extent the scientific
community ignored them. Probably the major reason for this lack of
attention stemmed from the philosophical position of most biologists
of the day. These men believed that living things were completely
different in basic make-up from non-living things in that they pos-
sessed some sort of mysterious "life force." It was incomprehensible
to many biologists to think of treating biological data mathematically
as Mendel did. As a matter of fact, one biological leader of the time
was so completely convinced that the idea was ridiculous that he re-
fused even to plant the seeds sent to him by Mendel as a verification
of his work.

In an apparently unrelated but, as will be seen later, very important effort in Germany, Meicher, a chemist, set up a laboratory on the banks of a large river where he began to study the chemical composition of the sperm of salmon, a common fish in the river. In the course of these studies he isolated a compound which, since it was found in the nucleus of cells and was acidic in nature, he termed nucleic acid; because of specific chemical properties, it was named deoxyribonucleic acid or DNA. This work, like Mendel's, became buried in the scientific literature since it appeared at the time to have little importance.

Shortly after the turn of the century another striking fact was noted. A comparison of the behavior of Mendel's "factors" (which by this time had been resurrected from the literature by three scientists working independently) with that of certain observable structures in cells called chromosomes revealed striking similarities. This observation lead Walter Sutton to postulate that there were indeed such things as factors (which still had not been seen and which soon became known as "genes"), and that they were associated in some way with the chromosomes of living cells.

Another major contribution was made by Thomas Hunt Morgan and his students during the twenty-year period ending in the 1930s. Morgan's work led him to the conclusion that "genes" not only existed and were located on the chromosomes, but that they were arranged in linear fashion almost like a string of beads. In essence, his reasoning followed the pattern already discussed of *"If* I assume that the genes are located in linear fashion on the chromosomes, *then* I can explain the results of my experiment."

Concurrent with Morgan's work, several chemists had turned their attention to DNA, the "useless" compound discovered by Meicher prior to 1900. By using new techniques they determined that DNA is composed of only six ingredients: adenine, thymine, cytocine, guanine, sugar, and phosphate. It was found, however, that important differences did occur in the amounts of these substances which were present in the DNA from different plants and animals. Despite these variations the amount of adenine always closely approximated the amount of thymine and the amount of cytocine was always almost exactly the same as that of guanine. At this point there was no explanation for this phenomenon and so these remained isolated facts.

Several experiments carried on in the 1940s and '50s began to attract a great deal of attention to the "new" compound DNA. In one of these Avery and McCloud, while working with the bacteria which causes pneumonia, made a startling discovery. These bacteria occur in two strains, one covered by a heavy capsule and the other not. Avery and McCloud crushed bacteria with capsules and added the resulting liquid to the medium on which some smooth coated (non-encapsulated) bacteria were growing. Surprisingly, when the cultures were examined a few days later it was found that the off-spring of the smooth coated bacteria were of the encapsulated variety. Since encapsulation is a genetic trait, and since smooth coated bacteria normally produce only smooth coated bacteria, it appeared that the heredity of the bacteria had actually been changed.

Further experiments revealed that the same result could be obtained by adding to the medium containing the smooth coated bacteria only the DNA which had been extracted from the encapsulated bacteria. This experiment, together with a number of others, was interpreted as indicating that DNA has many of the properties attributed by Mendel to his "factors." Indeed, it was thought that perhaps DNA was *the* substance of genes. The question remained, however, as to how biological information could be coded into a chemical substance and then expressed in specific traits.

In 1953 two scientists working in Britain tried to add the evidence resulting from experiments in which X-rays were beamed through DNA crystals to the chemical and biological facts described above. These men proposed a "model" for the DNA molecule which provided a reasonable explanation for its action. They proposed that the DNA molecule is shaped like a ladder that has been twisted. In their conception the uprights of the ladder are composed of alternating units of sugar and phosphate and the rungs are made up of the substances adenine, thymine, cytocine, and guanine. In their view each "rung" is composed of two of these substances and adenine is always paired with thymine and cytocine with guanine. Finally the assumption was made that the "base" pairs (the adenine-thymine, cytocine-guanine "rungs") occurred in a definite sequence in the chromosomes of a given plant or animal species and that this sequence varies from species to species. It was their contention that these variations in sequence represent the basic differences between different kinds of plants and animals.

Thus, the chromosomes came to be viewed as something like computer punch cards with base sequences replacing punched holes as the code. In the chromosomes of a dog egg the information "how to become a dog" is coded then in the form of the arrangement of four chemicals in the core of a large molecule.

The Watson-Crick suggestion as to the configuration of the DNA molecule and how it "acts as a gene" opened the door for a new surge of experimentation. Since the model was proposed in 1953 scientists have been addressing themselves to the questions of how the code in a DNA molecule is transmitted into biological reality and what the sequence of bases is which dictates a specific biological characteristic. The description of the results of this quest would require more space than is available here. For our purposes it is sufficient to say that remarkable progress has been made toward a theory of inheritance which is applicable to all living things from bacteria to elephants and from algae to redwood trees. This theory suggests that *biological* information is coded and distributed in a *mathematically* predictable manner, and is translated into specific *chemical* reactions leading to *physical* phenomena. Most of the research which is unveiling this pattern is being done with chemical and physical apparatus by scientists who must be biologists, chemists, physicists, and mathematicians all at the same time.

Despite the great strides made in describing the action of genes, it should be noted that no one has yet seen a gene nor does it appear now that they ever will.

The point of the gene story just related is that biology is now, in large measure, similar to the other sciences in its approach to solving nature's secrets. Its object is to generate theory which better explains a set of observations. As in the other sciences, the theory changes as the body of information which it explains grows larger. Perhaps the most important part of the story is the fact that it has not ended. It is just possible that a piece of "useless information" lies now in an obscure journal which a clever mind will some day use to reshape the story completely. One thing is certain: our concept of a "gene" will be different fifty years from now.

Implications for Biology Teaching

How does the concept of biology exemplified by the story of the gene theory compare with the one fostered by the traditional high school biology course? Unfortunately, the high school concept does not compare favorably. In essence, three things seem to be lacking:

1. Many of the pieces of information which have now been built into models by scientists are still treated in high school texts as if they were completely unrelated.
2. Where theories are treated, their tentativeness is neglected and they are taught as immutable laws.
3. The models which are taught are frequently outmoded ones which have been replaced by more encompassing conceptions.

An example relating to the gene story is perhaps in order. The typical high school graduate *is* exposed to the idea of a gene. The concept which he gets, however, is that genes are "blobs" strung along a chromosome in "string of beads" fashion. No attention is generally given to the reasoning which led Morgan to this general idea, or to the fact that it was proposed as a tentative conclusion to specific work and has now been supplanted. When more recent models of the gene *are* studied in high school, it is usually in the context that "DNA is" rather than "our present concept of DNA is."

Actually, there is nothing wrong with much of the information given in high school biology books. The problem stems from what is done with it. Many of the major generalizations (theories, models) of biology could be generated from the information already present in such courses, and the remainder could be included with the addition of certain recently revealed knowledge. Unfortunately, little attempt has been made in the past to organize the isolated facts so that students can see the "forest for the trees." In short, the content of high school biology courses is badly in need of being brought up to date and put to work. To be educationally sound, the facts of biology must be thought of as a *means* to an understanding of biological concepts, not as the *ends* which they have traditionally represented.

The Work of the Biological Sciences Curriculum Study

In 1958 the American Institute of Biological Sciences (AIBS), an organization composed of essentially all of the biologists in the United States, became concerned about the teaching of biology in American high schools. Several members of the organization had become acutely aware of the discrepancy between biology as it is practiced by biologists and as it is taught in the schools. They became convinced that improving this situation was a matter of the utmost urgency, and decided to undertake a major effort to produce a new approach to the teaching of high school biology.

In 1958 the AIBS received a grant from the National Science Foundation and established an organization which became known as the Biological Sciences Curriculum Study (BSCS). This group set up offices on the campus of the University of Colorado and during the next few years served as the stimulus through which a large number of the nation's outstanding biologists and biology teachers became involved in the production of new teaching and learning materials.

The materials developed here turned out to be considerably more than just another new biology book. They are currently in use by a substantial number of school systems across the United States and are being used as models by other textbook writers. It can literally be said that these materials are reshaping the entire pattern of biology teaching.

Because of the special nature of the materials, the qualifications of the individuals who produced them, and the amount of influence which they have already had and probably will continue to have on American biology teaching, no chapter on the teaching of modern biology could be complete without a description of the work of this important group.

The Organization of the BSCS Project

In reality much of the description of the organizational procedures of the PSSC physics group which were outlined in Chapter II could be inserted here as relevant to the BSCS attack on a similar problem. Indeed, perhaps the most important contribution made by the PSSC group was providing a prototype of an *approach* to curriculum development. As will be seen in the paragraphs which follow, the BSCS group, working largely in the summers, combined the talents of scientists and science teachers, used feedback from an intensive field testing program in making revisions, and in many other ways followed the PSSC plan. It should also be pointed out that, because of the experience of the PSSC group, the BSCS people were able to improve the plan somewhat.

Although the developmental plan of the BSCS biology program was generally similar to that originated by the physicists, the results were quite different. This being the case, the organizational aspects of the BSCS program will be discussed here in a limited way; we will concentrate instead upon the product of the project—specifically upon those characteristics which make the course unique.

The first job undertaken by the BSCS personnel was to identify the major content which should be included in a course in modern biology for high school students. A committee of biologists was charged with the responsibility of making this identification, and after a few meetings it became obvious that this was no simple task. Although rather quick general agreement was reached as to the kinds of content which should be included, there was considerable disagreement about the degree of emphasis which various concepts should receive and the sequence of presentation of topics.

As a result of these discussions, the committee decided that the specific sequence and emphasis in the materials to be produced were of relatively little importance, and that probably more than one good high school course in modern biology could and should be produced. As a matter of fact, they decided to try to develop three courses organized around the same broad content ideas, in each of which the individual writers were allowed to exercise their judgment and bring their interests and abilities to bear on the problem of the order of topics.

This thinking led the BSCS workers to produce three "versions" (not really three different courses) of a modern biology course organized around certain powerful biological ideas. These three programs became known, during their development, as the Blue, Yellow, and Green versions, and were subsequently published by three different commercial publishers under different titles.[1] The content themes which organize the three versions are as follows:

Change of living things through time—evolution.
Diversity of type and unity of pattern of living things.
Genetic continuity of life.
Complementarity of organism and environment.
Biological roots of behavior.
Complementarity of structure and function.
Regulation and homeostasis: the maintenance of life in the face of change.

---

[1] *Biological Science: Molecules to Man* (Blue Version), Houghton Mifflin Company, 1963, Boston, Massachusetts; *High School Biology: BSCS Green Version*, Rand McNally & Company, 1963, Chicago, Illinois; *Biological Science: An Inquiry Into Life* (Yellow Version), Harcourt, Brace & World Company, 1963, New York.

Science as inquiry.
Intellectual history of biological concepts.

If one examines the themes, particularly the last two, it is quite clear that the framers of the BSCS course considered the "processes of science" to be of equal importance in the content of a high school biology course with the more traditionally discussed subjects of genetics, embryology, etc.

Development of the BSCS "Version"

During the summer of 1960 three groups of professional biologists and high school teachers, in about equal numbers, gathered to produce materials. Each group was instructed to prepare a high school biology course based upon the themes described above. In essence, the three patterns which emerged tended to be organized around biology at the molecular level, biology from the ecological point of view, and biology which, its developers say, centers on the study of the cell. These patterns of emphasis became the Blue, Green, and Yellow versions of the course, respectively, and were continued into the final hardback publications.

The three versions which emerged from the initial writing conference were tried out in a large number of typical American high schools during the following year. Based upon the feedback from the teachers in these schools, the books were revised during a second writing conference which was conducted in the summer of 1961. This process was repeated in 1963 and final editions of the books, following extensive classroom testing and revision, were produced.

All of the three versions differed sharply in content from the typical high school biology book. In essence, traditional books tend to center on biology at the organismic level; that is to say, they center on the biology of the individual. The three BSCS books give considerably more emphasis to the chemistry of living things (biology at the atomic and molecular levels) and upon the biology involved in the association of several individuals (biology at the community and society levels). This means that the traditional topics of morphology (the gross structure of living things) and taxonomy (the process of classifying living things) receive considerably less attention in the BSCS books than had been the case previously.

A second major departure in these books is the emphasis on certain topics which have heretofore been considered "controversial." The BSCS approaches to biology all treat the subjects of evolution and human reproduction in a very straightforward manner. The topic of human reproduction is approached not as instruction in "sex education," but rather as an example of an important biological phenomenon. Evolution, since it was identified as one of the major organizing themes of biology, plays a central role in organizing the content of all three books. (As an interesting sidelight, except for minor flurries of sporadic, and in most cases ineffective, opposition the much feared reaction to the teaching of both evolution and reproduction has failed to materialize; the acceptance of those portions of the BSCS program which deal with them has been completely favorable.)

Other BSCS Activities

Although the three BSCS "versions" probably represent the most important contribution which the group has made to biology education (at least from the point of view of numbers of students affected), a number of other significant steps were carried out under the auspices of the study. Although these "other" programs have not had the impact that the "versions" have had, the techniques, approaches, and content are now having an influence on curriculum development at other than the high school levels and in subjects other than biology. They therefore merit close attention from the standpoint of secondary-school education as well as from the standpoint of education in biological science.

One of the major activities carried out by BSCS in addition to the development of the new three-version course is the so-called laboratory block program. The foundations for this program were laid down during the very early organizational meetings of the group. One of the first committees appointed was entitled "Innovations in Laboratory Instruction." This group was given the assignment of finding new ways of using the high school biology laboratory.

The major recommendation which came out of the Committee on Innovations in Laboratory Instruction was that there be developed a series of short, highly laboratory-centered "blocks" of material on significant biological topics. In the Committee's view, these blocks would be designed so that the student literally acted like a scientist for a period of time. The "blocks" were to consist of a series of tightly sequenced laboratory activities which could yield data appropriate to drawing highly significant conclusions.

The student would be given no textbook during the period of a given "block." He would not be lectured to by the teacher and he would be given very few conclusions; he would be forced to state hypotheses, carry out experiments designed to test them, analyze the data obtained from the experiments, and reach tentative conclusions. He would then carry the same procedure out again and try and come up with an overall conclusion relating the two sets of experiments. In this way it was hoped that the student, in a period of about six weeks, would derive for himself a number of the most important generalizations relating to a specific biological topic and gain considerable insight into the entire scientific approach to problem solving. Since very little emphasis would be placed upon specific information in these blocks, it was assumed that they would probably lead to quite different kinds of understandings than would the traditional high school book.

At the outset the Committee on Innovations in Laboratory Instruction recognized that this method of exploring biological topics was slow and time consuming. It was quite clear that one can "cover" biological material much more rapidly through a combination text-laboratory approach or through a textbook-lecture approach. Although the idea of "coverage" was of less concern to the BSCS group than has traditionally been the case, they recognized that a high school biology student should perhaps be exposed to more kinds of biological information than could possibly be provided through the "block" approach.

This thinking led ultimately to the idea of developing a series of several blocks dealing with important ideas that would be *supplementary* (or perhaps complementary) to a more traditional textbook. It was felt that a block on microbiology, for example, could be inserted by a teacher in his course at the same point that he would ordinarily cover microbiology. He would simply reduce or omit the coverage of that subject by the textbook and develop that particular topic by the more time-consuming block approach. This procedure would allow the teacher considerable freedom in choosing the subjects with which he would use the "block" approach, and would still provide for the degree of "coverage" needed, while allowing the stu-

dent to come into contact with the kind of experimentation which
the authors desired.

The report of the Committee on Innovations in the Use of Laboratories was acted on by the BSCS as one of its first decisions. A small
group of workers was commissioned to develop a series of blocks,
and the work proceeded at the University of Texas. The developers
of the laboratory blocks worked concurrently with the main body of
writers who were producing the versions. The blocks underwent two
revisions based upon feedback from trial schools and have now been
published in final form.[2]

They are written so that they can be used as parts of any biology
program but are particularly adapted to use with one of the three
BSCS versions.

The third facet of the initial BSCS program was the development
of a series of Invitations to Inquiry. Like the laboratory blocks, the
Invitations were written at the time that the three BSCS versions
were under production. Again, like the laboratory blocks, the Invitations are designed to be supplementary work which can be used
either with the BSCS books or with more traditional approaches.

The Invitations are actually a series of forty-four guided discussions of relevant biological topics. As their name implies, they are
designed to teach students how scientists deal with problems. Rather
than explain how the scientist operates, the Invitations create situations through guided questions which encourage the student to carry
out the desired operation.

The writers suggest that the Invitations may be used in three ways:
first, teachers might set aside a certain period every week as a time
for the discussion of the Invitations. In this situation the student
would have completed the complete series of Invitations in addition
to his regular biology work by the time his course is finished. Some
teachers use the Invitations as a supporting device for laboratory
instruction. In these cases the teacher selects an Invitation based
either upon the scientific skill which is developed or the content
which is being discussed and uses it to help the student in carrying
out a laboratory exercise. Finally, Invitations can be selected either
by process or content to supplement the non-laboratory portion of a
biology course. If, for example, the class is studying muscle contrac-

---

2 Laboratory Blocks are published by D. C. Heath & Company, Boston, Mass.
and by BSCS, the University of Colorado, Boulder.

tion, there are several Invitations to Inquiry which deal with this subject. The teacher might discuss these as part of his regular instructional program.

The Invitations to Inquiry have not as yet been published as a separate book. The present series of forty-four exercises has been published as part of the *Biology Teachers' Handbook* now published by John Wiley and Sons.[3]

Early in the tryout of the three BSCS versions it was clear that not all students do equally well with the courses. It appeared that the students in the middle of the population of those who normally take high school biology profited most from the instruction. While the slow learner found that the BSCS versions were quite difficult to understand, the really bright student was frequently unchallenged by the materials.

It was decided that it was an impossible task to produce a single biology course which was well suited to all levels of students. Clearly special courses of study were necessary for the gifted student and for the slow learner. Committees were established to produce materials for these groups of students. The gifted student committee decided that their problem could best be solved by producing supplemental materials rather than an entirely separate course. They felt that the regular versions could be satisfactory for gifted students provided that some highly challenging supplemental activities were available.

The committee members wrote to biologists all over the United States to ask them to submit prospectuses of individual research projects which might be carried out by high school students. The large number submitted were edited and the result was a two volume set of *Biological Investigations for Secondary School Students* published later under a different title.[4]

Each of the investigations was developed by a research biologist in a particular field of interest. Each outlines a particular problem which might be investigated by a high school student. The major unique feature of these investigations is the fact that they involve problems which have not as yet been solved by scientists.

Each investigation consists of three parts: a short background statement which sets the tone for the problem; either a statement of

[3] Joseph J. Schwab, *Biology Teachers' Handbook*. (New York: John Wiley & Sons, Inc., 1963).

[4] Paul Brandwein, *Research Problems in Biology: Investigations for Students,* Series 1 and 2. (New York: Doubleday & Company, 1963).

the specific problem or some suggestions as to what specific problems might be developed; and finally a suggested approach to solving the problem. In the suggested approach a line of reasoning and experimentation is proposed to give the student a departing point. With this information the student is given a reference list and told to proceed. These investigations are probably the most highly research-oriented materials published by any of the curriculum groups. It is assumed that any student who is not sufficiently challenged by the regular BSCS versions can be kept very gainfully occupied by doing one or more of these investigations.

Some teachers have used the investigations as the base for a second level biology course to follow first-year biology. That is to say, selected students (usually twelfth grade) are given several research problems to carry out essentially on their own. Such a second level course is presumed to provide the polish which a really talented biology student requires.

The group studying the problems of the slow learner decided that supplementary materials did not provide an answer to their problems. At the outset it was decided that the slow student should study the same type of biology that was developed in the BSCS versions; that is to say, a biology course for the slow learner should emphasize modern biology content and should give adequate opportunity for the student to learn the skills of inquiry which biological scientists use. The group felt that the major adjustments necessary to produce a course for slow learners were in pace and reading level. At this writing the group has conducted two summer writing conferences and one tryout of the materials, which have not as yet been released for widespread use.

The final activity in which the BSCS has become involved is the production of special monographs and special types of visual aids. Various biologists have been commissioned to write short précis on their research interests aimed at the high school biology teacher. These précis are published in soft cover form approximately six times per year.[5] The aim of the BSCS pamphlet series is to upgrade the high school teacher's knowledge of selected concepts and, over a long period, to upgrade his general knowledge of biology.

Unlike the PSSC physics group, the Biological Sciences Curriculum Study group has not made a wholesale attempt to produce edu-

---

[5] BSCS Pamphlet Series (Boston, Mass.: D. C. Heath & Company).

cational films. This, in part at least, stems from the fact that the American Institute of Biological Sciences has produced, as a result of another project, a series of 120 films dealing with modern biology. The BSCS group feels that many of these films are applicable to their program and that, therefore, further film work along these lines would be superfluous. They have, however, produced two types of special films: the techniques film and the single concept film. Both of these are somewhat specialized in character. The techniques films are short (about ten minutes or less) silent films in which a particular biological technique is demonstrated. One film, for example, shows how one handles fruitflies in conducting genetics experiments. The films are intended for the dual use of teacher training and helping students to master techniques which are used in the BSCS laboratory exercises. The single concept films, as their name implies, select a single major idea in biology and develop this in some detail. The ideas developed are those which either involve natural areas which may not be available to the teacher (a seacoast in Iowa, for example) or involve equipment and techniques not likely to be feasible for the high school laboratory. These again are designed to supplement student understanding of the BSCS textbooks.[6]

Basic Problems of Implementing Modern Biology Courses

Up to this point we have been dealing essentially with problems of objectives and of developing curriculum materials. Obviously, these are highly important ingredients in a successful biology program. But in themselves they will not solve the problems of biology education. The change in the objectives of biology teaching and the development of new materials have created a number of practical problems which, unless solved by the conscientious administrator and the classroom teacher, can be detrimental to the conduct of good modern programs. Many of these problems stem from the kind of laboratory facilities which are called for.

As has been pointed out, a course in modern biology must by definition be highly laboratory-centered. Furthermore, many of the experiments which are done in such courses involve the kind of laboratory equipment and furniture which has traditionally been

[6] BSCS Biological Techniques Film Series, Thorne Films, Inc., 1229 University Avenue, Boulder, Colorado, and BSCS Single Topic Films (not yet released).

available only to chemistry and physics teachers. Until a few years ago a well equipped biology laboratory consisted of plain tables and chairs, perhaps an aquarium, several charts and models, a variety of various kinds of "pickled" specimens, gear used to collect and kill specimens, a few microscopes, and a supply of the inevitable dissecting kits.

With modern courses such as those developed by the BSCS group, the appropriate laboratory should now contain such things as chemical glassware, standard chemical reagents, incubators, ovens, sterilizing equipment, a refrigerator, stand-up laboratory tables with acid proof tops, utilities (gas, water, and electricity) brought to the individual work station, and appropriate storage space. Without such equipment and furniture, the prospective teacher of a modern biology course is severely handicapped. In essence, if modern biology courses are to be taught, the equipment and furniture problems of biology teaching must be considered as equal to those facing the chemistry and physics teacher.

The second major problem which implementing a modern biology course often reveals is that of sequencing the science program. The traditional pattern for science courses at the high school level is tenth grade biology, eleventh grade chemistry, and twelfth grade physics. This pattern was established when biology was considered the "easy" science. Furthermore, it was felt that students should wait until they had had an opportunity to learn as much mathematics as possible before beginning chemistry and physics. It should be quite clear to the reader by this point that biology has now come to depend very heavily upon the chemistry and physics which traditionally follow it.

To date, the problem of providing a chemistry and physics background for biology students has been solved by building into a modern biology course enough training in physical science to allow the student to progress. This leads to a rather spotty treatment of the chemistry; in some cases the student acquires understandings in the tenth grade biology course that the eleventh grade chemistry teacher must "unteach." This unsatisfactory situation occurs because the biology teacher tends to teach chemistry as a "tool" and some of the intellectual beauty of the physical sciences is lost.

There are essentially two other ways of attacking this problem. First, that biology might conceivably be made a twelfth grade subject following courses in chemistry and physics in the tenth and eleventh grades. With the advent of modern mathematics programs at the elementary, junior high, and high school levels, this could probably be made defensible to the physical scientists. Unfortunately, however, such a move would bring with it certain difficulties. If the twelfth grade biology course required chemistry and physics as prerequisites (and if it did not, why teach it at this level?), the percentage of students taking the course would probably drop from about ninety percent at present to perhaps twenty-five percent. Many students would graduate from high school with no biology background whatsoever. (One of the great educational tragedies is that many now graduate from high school with no physics or chemistry.) Even the least zealous biology teacher is not interested in losing his audience.

A second possibility for a solution lies not in the high school but in the junior high school. To date very little has been done in developing science programs for this level. If the present trend of emphasizing basic science concepts at the pre-college level continues, it seems logical that the kinds of physical science understandings required of a biology student could be given during his junior high school years. Without question, the junior high school science program, whatever pattern it takes, will ultimately include concepts such as the atomic nature of matter, energy, force, and laws of chemical combinations. With adequate preparation the tenth grade student should be able to cope reasonably well with the kinds of ideas dealt with in modern biology. This would seem to be the best answer to the problem.

CHAPTER IV

Chemistry: The Many Faces of Structure

The chapters dealing with the teaching of physics and biology revealed two approaches to the development of curriculum which, despite their differences, have many things in common. Chapter II, on Physics, presented a case history of curriculum development, showing how one group of people approached the job and how they proceeded. In describing the recent activity in biology, Chapter III pointed up the great differences between what biology *is* and what students in high school *think* it is—differences which are due largely to the newness of biology as a "real science."

In our analysis of high school chemistry, a different theme will be emphasized, for in this field there are two new high school courses. Both have been developed by responsible scientists working in much the same way. Both reflect recent developments in the science, and both ignore much that has been included in past courses in chemistry. Yet the differences between the two courses are fundamental. This causes some concern to high school teachers and especially to school administrators who must participate in decisions regarding curricula often without sufficient background in science to understand the courses being compared. The reasons which underlie the development of two new courses are of interest in the present chapter; more specifically, the *structure* of the science will be examined as we look for an answer to the question, why two new courses in chemistry?

The Historical Development of Chemistry

Before considering the details of structure in high school chemistry, it will be helpful to examine briefly the history of chemistry itself for, as in physics, the development of the science has influenced the manner in which it has been taught. The science of chemistry, as opposed to the alchemy of earlier centuries, came to life in 1789 with the publication of Lavoisier's *Elements of Chemistry*. Prior to that time little was known about the composition of matter or the combinations of substances. Lavoisier showed the importance of quantitative methods in the chemistry laboratory; he introduced the principle of the conservation of matter by stating that nothing was gained or lost in the course of a chemical reaction. It was Lavoisier who also added the weight of his opinion to the ancient idea that the elements were substances and could not be broken down into simpler materials.

Following Lavoisier's work, there was increased interest in the more fundamental laws of chemistry, especially those attempting an explanation of chemical reaction and the structure of matter, originated in the early part of the Nineteenth Century. John Dalton's atomic theory in 1800 gave early scientists an insight into the nature of elementary particles and, over the years, this theory has been polished and refined in an attempt to describe the atom, its structure, and behavior. But the present picture of the atom is far from complete and to this day there is no model of the atom which can explain satisfactorily all of its known properties. We now consider early attempts to explain the atom to be crude and obsolete; perhaps fifty years from now our present ideas will also be out-of-date.

Toward the end of the nineteenth century chemistry began to advance at a rapid pace, especially in the discovery of new elements. As the amount of new information mounted, chemistry became divided into several "branches." Each of these branches, especially organic chemistry, the study of carbon and its compounds, required the development of new tools and techniques.

In the early Twentieth Century chemistry as a science became more and more dependent upon advances in physics. With the discovery of radioactivity by Becquerel and the isolation of radium by Madame Curie, a new door was opened to an important area of chemistry and physics. In the first half of the century chemists turned their attention to development of new industrial processes and products. Both World Wars brought on pressures which resulted in new and striking developments—for example, high powered explosives in World War I and the sulfa drugs in World War II. The pace of chemistry, like that of the other natural sciences, continues to accelerate and today even the most skeptical would not predict that the end is in sight.

Chemistry in the Schools

The teaching of chemistry in the schools has been tied up closely with the development of chemistry itself. Until the beginning of the Nineteenth Century, there was no attempt whatever to teach chemistry in the schools. After the time of Lavoisier and Priestly the subject began to appear in the public high school which was then just coming onto the scene. The first chemistry was doubtless taught by lectures and recitation with some demonstrations by the instructor. In the middle Nineteenth Century chemistry was described as the branch of science most suitable for girls and "a good chemical apparatus" was often advertised by the schools as a lure to young women who were headed for college.

With the rise of the academies in this country the teaching of chemistry flourished; during the first forty years of the Nineteenth Century it was taught in a rapidly increasing number of schools. The lack of laboratory equipment (most of which was purchased from Great Britain) and textbooks was a serious problem. During the second half of the century laboratory work was given increasing emphasis. The colleges began to require high school science courses for entrance; Harvard College in 1872 was the first to establish such a requirement and it soon spread to most of the others. Some colleges provided lists of required experiments along with courses of study which the high schools followed. By the end of the Nineteenth Century, most courses in chemistry included considerable emphasis on laboratory work.

During this period the value of chemistry in agriculture, medicine, and in other practical ways was increasingly recognized. Its major support came from those who saw its functional applications. This spirit continuing into the Twentieth Century, was augmented by the technological demands of both World Wars.

High School Chemistry—A Traditional Course

In a companion volume by Seymour Fowler considerable attention is given to present high school science offerings.[1] It will be useful in this book to examine a traditional high school chemistry

---

[1] H. Seymour Fowler, *Secondary School Science Teaching Practices* (New York: The Center for Applied Research in Education Inc., 1964).

course but only for purposes of comparison of the old course with the new. We will look closely at the kind of course used in the great majority of American high schools up until about 1962. (While there is, of course, some variation among courses offered throughout the United States, there is nevertheless a somewhat standard pattern in the majority of schools.)

The introductory chapters of the textbook probably deal primarily with matter and energy and serve to familiarize the students with the composition of matter and the metric system of measurement. The student is then plunged into a study of atomic structure and the nature of chemical classification leading to the concept of atomic numbers and the periodic table. The periodic table, a systematic listing of the 103 known elements and some of their properties, is partially memorized by the student.

The ability of atoms to combine to form molecules, the combining capacity of different elements, and the notion of valence are then considered. With this background, the student is introduced to formula writing and the naming of compounds, again memorizing many of the more common formulae.

After this introduction, oxygen and hydrogen, their physical and chemical properties, and the methods of their laboratory and industrial preparation are usually studied in turn. The laws which describe the behavior of gases (Charles' and Boyle's Laws) are presented and the student must solve mathematical problems involving the temperature, pressure, and volume of gases. This is usually accomplished by relating certain information and data to a set of conventional formulae for solving the problem. Finally, the familiar compound of oxygen and hydrogen—water—is studied. The student is concerned with its physical properties, the structure of the water molecule, the nature of the bond which holds the molecule together, and the chemical behavior of water. Methods of water purification are also investigated.

The student then begins serious work with chemical calculations. He must understand the concept of molecular weight and be able to find the percentage composition of a compound. Here again, emphasis is often given to industrial applications, such as finding the percentage of iron in a sample of ore. He learns how to determine the empirical formula of a compound. He also learns how to write and balance chemical equations and is introduced to the four general types of chemical reactions. At this point the concept of energy change in chemical reactions is presented, although most traditional courses treat the topic superficially. Weight relations in chemical reactions are then taken up followed by a study of the molecular composition of gases. The student then studies volume relations in chemical reactions and is required to solve the usual volume-volume and weight-volume problems.

A unit is usually included on carbon and its compounds and includes a study of the forms of carbon, crystal structure, and the industrial production of carbon products such as charcoal and coke. It includes also a study of the oxides of carbon and finally introduces the student briefly to structural formulae and the different series of hydrocarbons.

The theory of ionization-acids, bases and salts, chemical equilibrium, and the electron transfer involved in oxidation and reduction are usually taken up at this point.

The chemistry of the active metals—sodium and calcium and their close relatives—are studied. The Solvay process for the preparation of sodium carbonate is described and, following the usual pattern, there is considerable emphasis on industrial processes.

The halogen family and sulfur and its oxides and acids are also taken up, followed by a study of the nitrogen family including phosphorous, arsenic, antimony, and bismuth. The nitrogen cycle and its industrial applications are described along with the properties of ammonia, nitric acid and the nitrogen products such as fertilizers and explosives.

A unit is usually devoted to the light structural metals—beryllium, magnesium, aluminum, and titanium—with subsequent chapters on the iron family, the copper family, zinc, cadmium, mercury, tin, and lead. Emphasis is usually placed on the metallurgy, properties, and uses of these heavy metals and on their importance to man in a modern industrial society. The processes for making steel are described in detail.

The more recent "traditional" texts usually include a unit dealing with natural and artificial radioactivity. It begins with the discovery of radioactivity and especially the work of the Curies in discovering radium. Alpha particles and gamma rays, which represent the energy release in radioactive decay, are described. In the discussion of artificial radioactivity such concepts as binding energy, chain reaction, critical mass, electron-volt, fission, fusion, nuclear reactor, and radioactive fallout are defined and used. To be sure, in the limited amount of space available they are often incompletely defined and sparingly used.

The production of man-made elements by neutron bombardment, the production of new products by fission, and the separation of uranium isotopes are studied. Einstein's famous equation, $E = mc^2$, is almost invariably given; however, a study leading to its real meaning is apt to be missing.

A final unit on industrial and commercial applications is usually included. This unit devotes attention to such topics as detergents, soaps, alcohols, paper, textiles, rubber, and plastic, with particular emphasis on industrial processes for their production and on ways in which they have changed our way of life.

The hypothetical chemistry textbook described above is fairly typical of high school chemistry textbooks in use in this country. It is supposedly an all-purpose book designed to meet the varying needs of the high school chemistry course: to prepare for the study of chemistry in college and to help provide a broad understanding of science for the student who will not go to college.

The textbook described above is usually supplemented by films and a set of laboratory experiments. The films, for the most part, describe the preparation of specific compounds, or they relate chemistry to our society, or they show laboratory techniques. The laboratory, which usually takes one period per week of the student's time, centers around a laboratory manual which generally complements the textbook. The students are probably given rather specific directions for carrying out exercises which verify certain things they have already learned from either the textbook or the teacher. For example, the students nearly always prepare oxygen gas by heating potassium chlorate and manganese dioxide following the step-by-step directions given in the manual. After obtaining the gas, they test it for its properties, again following specific instructions in the manual, to verify the properties already described in the text ("supports combustion, slightly soluble in water, odorless, colorless, etc."). The students' "observations" are recorded in the laboratory manual, usually by filling in blanks in prefabricated sentences. They are then often asked to answer a few general questions based on the experience gained in the laboratory. Some emphasis may be given to safety in the laboratory and to the mechanical manipulation of equipment. It is generally true that, while the traditional chemistry student may develop little initiative by following a step-by-step laboratory procedure, he is given opportunity to develop good laboratory technique. He becomes familiar with the equipment in the laboratory and should know how to use it.

Let us now return to a consideration of structure. One structural base for the traditional chemistry course described above might be the historical one, for indeed, some of the earliest ideas from the history of chemistry appear near the beginning of the course: the combining capacity of different substances; an interest in oxygen and its properties; the properties of gases which were of such great interest to Lavoisier and Priestly; the laws describing the behavior of confined gases; the emphasis on chemical calculations; and the writing and balancing of equations. The authors might have reasoned that the most basic ideas in chemistry did indeed come first in its historical development and such an approach, therefore, is a logical one in presenting chemistry to high school students—and at first glance this argument appears to have a good deal of force.

The historical approach to sequence is unfortunately not generally the best when all aspects of learning are considered. Its major drawback is that it is not economical. If each important concept in the chemistry course were to be developed historically, the textbook would doubtless be several thousand pages in length, for a reasonably complete account of the sequence of events adds up to a rather long story—and to leave out any major ideas in the story based on the historical approach would be to leave noticeable gaps in the account. Another problem is that ideas often appear "out of turn"; that is, they appear before the discovery of another concept from which the earlier one might have been more easily and more meaningfully developed. The curriculum developer of today has the advantage of historical hindsight and it is an advantage which he should use in presenting chemistry to students.

Another structural base for the traditional course might have been the technological one. An examination of the course described above reveals considerable emphasis on the uses of chemistry in the modern world, particularly as the course progresses. It could be claimed that the emphasis on fundamental chemistry early in the course serves mostly the purpose of enabling the student to understand the technological applications which come later and which represent the real substance of the course.

In truth, the structure of the traditional chemistry course is based on a combinaiton of approaches. They include the history of chemistry, the technology of the modern scientific world, the college entrance requirements, the urgency to teach the important elements of modern chemistry, and the need to present a cross-section of all of chemistry to give the students a "complete" understanding of this branch of science. But this approach to the structure of the chemistry course—or any one of those listed above taken separately—represents, at best, an artificial approach to the problem of structure. Perhaps the most important element in the learning situation is not taken into account at all: the "intellectual" approach. If chemistry as one of man's important pursuits during the last several centuries has any appeal for its own sake, the appeal to man's natural curiosity ought to be exploited. And if, as the authors of one of the new curricula in chemistry to contend, "chemistry is inherently fascinating," then it should be possible to develop a course which would follow "the major paths by which a chemist proceeds in his dealings with chemical phenomena." And it ought to be possible "to produce a reasoned argument for the topics to be included or excluded, the order of presentation, and the points at which individual narration might most readily be introduced."[2]

Chemistry, unlike biology and physics, has seen two major curriculum-reform efforts at the high school level. The first of these, the Chemical Bond Approach (CBA) project, was conceived in 1958; and the second, the Chemical Education Materials Study (CHEMS) was started in 1960. Each of these programs has been developed by a number of the country's outstanding chemists and educators and each departs in various important ways from the traditional structure of high school chemistry. Let us examine these in turn.

The Chemical Bond Approach (CBA) Course

In June, 1957, a conference sponsored by the Division of Chemical Education of the American Chemical Society and the Crown-

[2] Lawrence E. Strong and M. Kent Wilson, "Chemical Bonds: A Central Theme for High School Chemistry," *Journal of Chemical Education*, XXXV (February, 1958), 56. (Dr. Strong, Professor of Chemistry at Earlham College, Richmond, Indiana, is Director of the Chemical Bond Approach Project.)

Zellerbach Foundation was conducted at Reed College in Portland, Oregon, for the purpose of discussing the integration of high school and college chemistry courses. In attendance were fifteen high school teachers and eighteen college teachers from all sections of the country and from small schools as well as large. This conference considered the efforts of a number of organizations in this country to improve high school and college chemistry teaching. One of the outcomes of this conference according to Strong and Wilson was ". . . that a good high school chemistry course ought to have a quality of intellectual integrity that can be communicated to the student and that this could be achieved by having a focus toward which most of the discussion could be directed. If a course for high school students could be devised with a central theme less broad than the whole of chemistry, but including the major paths by which a chemist proceeds in his dealings with chemical phenomena, then it ought to be possible to produce a reasoned argument for the topics to be included or excluded, the order of presentation, and the points at which individual narration might most readily be introduced."[3] In an effort to produce such a reasoned argument for the topics to be included in a high school chemistry course, the authors point out that the concept of chemical bonds could serve as a unifying, central theme. If the high school student can be made to understand one of the most basic ideas in chemistry, if he understands that many of the properties exhibited by substances are determined by the nature of atomic bonds rather than by the specific properties of the atoms themselves—for example, if the student can understand that the color of a material is dependent upon the chemical bonds which link its atoms together—then he has some of the insight of the chemist.

The following paragraph is taken from an expository statement distributed by the CBA project early in its history; it presents the major ideas in this new approach:

> If there is any one characteristic of the basis for CBA Chemistry, it is probably the belief that chemistry is inherently fascinating and that this fascination can be seen by students early in their exposure to the subject. To reveal the fascination, it is not enough, however, to have the student memorize the data of chemistry. Indeed, we would argue that chemistry is more than the facts which make up the information possessed by chemists. Rather, chemistry as prac-

---

[3] *Ibid.*

ticed is a powerful process for uncovering and extending natural phenomena. . . .[4]

In the CBA laboratory program, the student does some of his most important work; not only does he collect data but he also applies ideas to these data. The experiments are often presented as puzzles and the student's interest in them might well be described as puzzle fascination. Separate information from the laboratory and from the student's reading fit together into a logical scheme which involves the use of stated assumptions and, in some cases, mental models. Frequently, the solution to the problem—or perhaps the appearance of additional problems along the way—suggests other paths for the student to explore and he is encouraged to follow up such extensions of his research. This attempt to aid the student in his study of the interaction of conceptual schemes with the observation and experiment carried out in the laboratory characterizes the CBA approach.

It must be pointed out, however, that laboratory experiments should not automatically lead to a pre-determined conclusion. Rather the student must develop his own argument for his findings and this argument should be an important outcome of the exercise. Quantitative data which can be reproduced are less important in this approach to laboratory work than in most traditional chemistry courses although the importance of accurate data gathering and the proper use of mathematics is not minimized. In certain experiments there is a deliberate attempt to acquaint the student with the more important laboratory techniques but this is presented in the context of the student's attempt to solve a particular problem.

The CBA staff, in further describing the laboratory experiments, states that the main criteria for an effective laboratory experiment are the tightness with which it fits into the text, its capacity to involve the student in acquiring data and executing a logical argument, and its capacity for contributing to subsequent discussions throughout the course.

The CBA course makes much of mental models. The first of these appears in the initial experiment and is concerned with a scientific "black box." In this experiment, an unknown object is sealed within a closed box and presented to the student who, naturally, finds that

---

[4] Chemical Bond Approach, *CBA Newsletter* (Richmond, Indiana: Earlham College, February, 1961), p. 1.

he cannot determine the properties of the object in the box through visual observation or direct handling. This "black box," then, is analogous to a system the composition and operation of which are not apparent to the outside observer. It may be possible, however, to gain some information on the box's contents. Operations such as tilting the box at various angles, shaking it, rotating it, applying a magnet to the sides of the box, and similar tests may be applied. On the basis of these manipulations, certain assumptions about the contents of the box can be made. The student is reminded that these assumptions are based upon experimental evidence but they must, nevertheless, be considered tentative and subject to revision upon further experimentation. From the total group of observations and assumptions, a model of the contents may be proposed which may or may not be an accurate representation of the items in the box; in any case the student has approached this problem in much the same way as he would approach a scientific problem where he has limited information available. The use of mental models plays an important part in the work of natural scientists, especially chemists and physi cists.

Extending the idea that substances can be roughly classified by their properties, Volume I of the CBA textbook[5] identifies three different types of bonds between atoms. These are ionic, metallic, and covalent bonds. Volume I then sets out to show how the notions about chemical bonds are powerful aids to understanding the structures and reactions of substances. It calls heavily upon the concept of energy and energy exchange in chemical reactions.

In the first chapter the student explores the science of chemistry itself and seeks to find the answers to such questions as, what is a scientist? what is science? what is chemistry? what is matter? and what are its properties? He is introduced to the nature of elements and compounds, atoms and molecules, and finally is asked to consider several important questions which arise when one attempts to understand the nature of chemical change. These include: (1) Why do some combinations of elements exist and not others? (2) Why do some changes occur while others do not? (3) Why do some changes take place quickly and others slowly? (4) How do temperature, pressure, and composition affect chemical change?

---

[5] *Chemical Systems,* Chemical Bond Approach Project (New York: McGraw-Hill Book Co., 1964).

In Chapter II of the textbook and also in the second experiment which involves the use of density as an identifying property, the student is directed to the idea that chemical reactions raise questions which cannot be answered by experiment alone, and that chemistry and the equipment of chemistry must sometimes be regarded as black boxes the inner workings of which cannot be completely understood by laboratory investigation.

In Chapter IV the student is led to the development of an atomic and molecular model based on assumptions and on his own logic; this model is arrived at by the application of the "black box" approach. Since this model does not deal with all aspects of matter, a second model is added in the following chapter to deal with Kinetic Molecular Theory. The CBA group explains that the first model is for structure and the second for disorder and that the application of the two together will be useful in Chapter VI for a systematic discussion of several reactions.

The CBA authors, in attempting to explain the major ideas and purposes set forth in the textbook and laboratory guide, have shown something of the unique nature of the CBA course:

> As the student enters into the process of combining facts and ideas, he should raise questions of various kinds. Thus in the reaction of methane and oxygen, why does the methane react with oxygen but not nitrogen? If methane burns in air there is plenty of nitrogen but no perceptible reaction takes place. Why not? A comparison of methane and neon reveals that each of them has the same number of electrons and protons per molecule. Why then are they different? Models are quite helpful in providing some of the answers.[6]

In addition to the emphasis on models and their use in understanding the major concepts in chemistry, other innovations are introduced and other threads developed, such as electrostatics. The description of some of the electrical properties of matter beginning in Chapter III leads quickly to Coulomb's law—treated lightly if at all in traditional chemistry textbooks—which is useful at this point and also in later chapters. In Chapter IV some assumptions about the nature of electrons are used to deduce the structure of atoms and molecules. This thread is also important in later chapters where atomic and molecular structure are considered further. In Chapters

---

[6] Chemical Bond Approach Project, *CBA Newsletter loc. cit.*, p. 1.

X and XI ionic substances and periodicity are discussed with Coulomb's law serving as a governing principle throughout.

One of the most important concepts in all of physical science is the understanding of what energy is and what it does. It is given an extended treatment in the CBA course: it is another thread which runs through much of the course. When chemical reactions as laboratory phenomena are introduced early in the course, the student notes that a temperature change usually accompanies a chemical change and this observation is interpreted in terms of energy transfer. This concept, used increasingly in subsequent chapters, becomes an important theme in the same sense as chemical bonds. The conservation of energy—the notion that energy cannot be created or destroyed—is given major attention in the CBA course as it is in all others.

The careful observer can detect other threads which run through the CBA course. These threads, according to the authors, are designed to do more than simplify teaching strategy. They are designed to help the student see the "importance of organizing his own information and recognizing not only those parts which fit neatly together, but also tag ends which are often intriguing because they don't quite fit."[7]

The textbook and the laboratory guide are closely correlated and are intended to be supplementary and complementary. By frequently shifting his attention from the classroom to the laboratory, the student learns to recognize the most efficient means of studying different topics. Just as the chemist makes a clear distinction between what is observable and what is deduced from the information at hand, the student becomes aware of the variety of tools available for studying a problem; and he learns to select that which is most suitable.

The laboratory guide emphasizes real experimentation. Students are asked to investigate problems related to the observed characteristics of selected chemical systems. Students are not required to obtain a "right" answer or merely to observe, for example, that a precipitate forms or a color change occurs. Both in the laboratory and in the classroom there is continuous emphasis on the interplay between thought, idea, and experiment.

---

[7] *Ibid.*, p. 2.

The experimental nature of the course is enhanced by the use of actual experimental data in the text. Many tables and graphs are direct reports of experiments utilizing equipment and procedures that a high school student could set up. The solving of arithmetical problems is emphasized in the classroom as well as in the laboratory and definitions are arrived at from experimental data throughout the course.

In both the text and the laboratory guide, students are encouraged to plan their experimental procedures in order to use their laboratory time most effectively. The three groups of experiments in the guide are divided generally into (1) those that all students can and should do, (2) those that some students will have the time and interest to do, (3) those which only the most capable students will undertake.

The Chemical Education Materials Study (CHEMS) Course

The second large-scale chemistry curriculum project is the Chemical Education Materials Study (CHEMS), which began work in January, 1960, and continued until 1963, at which time a hard-covered textbook was completed and published commercially.[8] Again the question arises, "What is the significance of two approaches to the teaching of high school chemistry? Are the CBA and CHEM Study groups in competition to determine which method is superior and should, therefore, be adopted by America's high schools?" In answer to these questions, each group has been quick to disclaim any competition with the other. Both point out that there are likely many ways to teach high school chemistry and that it would be well to explore several of them. They have expressed the desire to try out numerous ideas and to make it easy for others to adopt and adapt from them. While they have not said so, it is nonetheless true that the particular flavor of each course represents in large measure the peculiar preferences of the chemists who were most influential in establishing the course's general direction or central theme.

The organization of the course is easily described. The first third of the course is devoted to an overview of chemistry; the second third investigates the following major topics: energy and chemical

---

[8] *Chemistry, An Experimental Science,* Chemical Education Materials Study (San Francisco: W. H. Freeman & Company, 1963).

reactions, rates of chemical reactions, equilibrium and chemical reactions, acids and bases, oxidation-reduction, ionic reactions, stoichiometry, atoms and their structure, periodicity of chemical properties, and electronic structure. The last third of the course consists of a more detailed exploration of these and also treats such topics as organic chemistry, biochemistry, and chemistry of the earth and other planets.

The CHEM Study course is generally considered to be highly experimental in its approach, perhaps more so than the CBA course and certainly more so than traditional courses. Its experimental nature is emphasized to the student in his first contact with the course: his first laboratory experiment consists of making careful observations of a burning candle. The student is asked to write down in five or ten minutes what he observes. As a homework assignment he is asked to revise his written record of the burning candle and to bring this to class the following day. His teacher has been instructed not to give him his textbook until the second day, whereupon he finds in the book a three-page appendix entitled "Description of a Burning Candle." This description includes fifty-three different observations whereas experience has shown that most students list between six and twelve. After the description of what a chemist sees when he observes a burning candle, the appendix includes the following statement:

1. The description is comprehensive in qualitative terms. Did you include mention of appearance? smell? taste? feel? sound? (Note: A chemist quickly becomes reluctant to taste or smell an unknown chemical. A chemical should be considered to be poisonous unless it is known not to be!)

2. Wherever possible, the description is stated quantitatively. This means the question "How much?" is answered (the quantity is specified). The remark that the flame emits yellow light is made more meaningful by the "how much" expression, "bright but not blinding." The statement that heat is emitted might lead a cautious investigator who is lighting a candle for the first time to stand in a concrete blockhouse one hundred yards away. The few words telling him "how much" heat would save him this overprecaution.

3. The description does not presume the importance of an observation. Thus the observation that a burning candle does not emit sound deserves to be mentioned just as much as the observation that it does emit light.

4. The description does not confuse observations with interpreta-

tions. It is an observation that the top of the burning candle is wet with a colorless liquid. It would be an interpretation to state the presumed composition of this liquid.[9]

According to Dr. J. Arthur Campbell, the Director of the original CHEM Study group, it is important even at this very early stage in the course to have the student distinguish between what he sees and what he thinks his observations mean. The discussion by the class of the burning candle observation after several days of laboratory work touches on such things as the role of the wick and the possibility of isolating an intermediate in a chemical reaction, namely the soot. (Very little soot can be found at the top of the candle, yet it is possible to find a great deal in the candle flame.)

During this initial week the course is conducted entirely in the laboratory. The student follows up each unanswered question as it occurs in an experiment. For example, in the initial observation of the burning candle, the question often arises, "What is the colorless liquid in the bowl at the top of the burning candle?" Perhaps it is just melted wax, but how do you know? The student then proceeds to compare the behavior of several different substances when heated and finds that each substance melts at a specific temperature and in an order that does not vary. This observation leads the student into an investigation of the melting point of a "pure" substance—paradichlorobenzene (moth crystals)—used because of its ready availability and its purity. (It is worth noting that most CHEM Study laboratory exercises are designed around simple equipment and materials in order that the student's total attention may be focused on the question he is investigating and not on complicated and cumbersome equipment.) The student collects data on the melting and cooling behavior of the paradichlorobenzene and plots heating and cooling temperatures against time. The resulting graph gives him his first hint as to the relationship between energy and chemical systems. Students are generally quick to notice the heat effects involved as the candle changes from a liquid to a solid form. With this in mind, they next measure the heat of combustion and heat of solidification of candle wax. The data obtained in this experiment allow the student to predict the total amount of heat energy, in calories, contained in the candle. At this point the textbooks are passed out and the formal part of the CHEM Study course begins.

---

[9] *Ibid.,* p. 450.

Through the candle experiment the students are introduced at a very early stage in the chemistry course to the following basic concepts: mechanisms of reactions, rate of reactions, energy release and activation energies, phase changes, and reaction products. Perhaps the most important idea of all is for the student to discover that systems appearing to be simple may really not be so simple after all —but that they can be comprehended in simple terms.

In explaining some of the laboratory experiments and their purposes, Dr. Campbell points to the emphasis on quantitative experiments and the organization of the material in such a way that, as often as possible, the student carries out an experiment in the laboratory before he reads a full discussion of it in the textbook. He is thus able to proceed into the unknown on his own and to make his own discoveries using the text to tie them together. CHEM Study teachers report that students display unusual enthusiasm when they fit the last piece into the puzzle, thereby "discovering" an important chemical concept.

There is much emphasis on atomic and molecular forces and, as in the CBA course, on the use of mental models. Considerable stress is placed on the great disparity of numbers involved in any chemical system—the vast quantity of atoms and molecules and their very small sizes.

The CHEM Study approach also emphasizes the concept of energy and its role in chemical reactions. The idea of systems tending to reach maximum randomness and attain minimum energy is introduced. Chemical reactions are studied in terms of the kinetics and reaction mechanisms—what the arrows or equal signs in the questions represent. The concept of dynamic equilibrium as one of chemistry's fundamental ideas is presented.

Somewhat to the dismay of the traditional chemistry teacher, the concept of the atom is not considered until the student is well into the middle of the CHEM Study course. With a working background of chemical kinetics, thermodynamics, and some insight into the properties of the elements, the student is better prepared to benefit from and appreciate a thorough study of the atom.

Experimental evidence is given for the existence of the atom and its sub-atomic components. The student is then introduced to quantum mechanics as a tool for understanding the atom. This approach is quite sophisticated for a high school chemistry course, and leads to a study of the most recent ideas and theories concerning atomic structure.

With a better understanding of atoms the student now studies molecules in the gas phase, where he is introduced to molecular architecture and chemical bonding. The study of chemical bonding is carried into solids and liquids where Van derWaal's ionic, co-valent, and metalic bonds are investigated. Throughout this section, strong correlation is shown between the properties of the elements and their systematic arrangement in the periodic table.

Generally, this study of atoms and molecules rounds out the course. Many questions which the student has had since the begin-ning of the school year suddenly become answered—again, with the student "discovering" the answer for himself. Several chapters are then presented which reconsider the elements, now conveniently grouped, according to their properties, into families. Fortified with his knowledge of chemical structure—not only electron structure, but the size, shape, and arrangement of atoms and molecules and the forces acting within them—and thinking in terms of energy, the student is now in a position to understand some fundamental chem-istry.

It is clearly evident from an examination of the CBA and CHEM Study courses that their structural base is quite different from that of the traditional chemistry course and their appeal to the students is of an entirely different nature. They have ignored almost entirely the sequence of events in the history of chemistry; they have paid scant attention to the modern-day technological applications of chemistry to the scientific world in which the student lives; they have made no attempts whatever to give "complete" coverage to the field of chem-istry; and they have left untouched a great many of the subjects which heretofore have been considered essential in any acceptable high school chemistry course.

What they have done has been to develop courses which attempt to show the beauty and order in chemistry as chemists view it; they have seized the most fundamental ideas in the discipline and have built around them conceptual schemes which honestly reflect the chemical behavior of matter. Above all, they have attempted to ap-peal to the student's intellect, to challenge him at the point where he is the most vulnerable—his innate curiosity about the natural world —and they have taken pains to lead him along a careful path where the key to an understanding of the next idea is an understanding of the preceding one; in other words, where the student's curiosity is not for isolated bits of information with their appeal of gadgetry, but for the organization, the neatness, the periodicity that is inherent in the science itself. As is the case with physics and biology, the student must go beyond the information given to infer relationships among elements in the situation; he is encouraged to regard theory as theory and not as fact; he is repeatedly reminded that chemistry is not a descriptive science but is both speculative and quantitative; and, above all, he sees chemistry as a basic science discipline, not as a body of technological applications. And as in physics, it is from this base, on which the developers of the new curricula have attempted to build their structure, that the student should be able to cope with the variety of life situations which he faces in the world of science in which he lives.

The CBA and CHEM Study courses have been tested at length in the high schools and revised several times on the basis of these tests. Both are now published commercially and are used in a substantial number of American high schools. The question of whether CBA or CHEM Study chemistry is better for high school students has not been settled in the minds of most educators and, indeed, of most chemists. If this question is ever answered, the answer will be found only after extended classroom testing. The important point, however, is that there is no real competition between proponents of the two courses to have one adopted to the exclusion of the other. Instead, both courses are believed by thoughtful educators to represent worthy approaches to the study of chemistry and each likely has its own unique strengths. The important question is, which course does the chemistry teacher feel most comfortable with? Which more nearly represents his own sympathies and its own interests in chemistry? Which seems more nearly to reflect the educational goals of the school?

The new courses, without doubt, have much to commend them. They have been produced by some of the best minds in chemistry with the aid of experienced high school teachers and others in professional education. As with the new curricula in physics and biology, they have benefited from the collective energies of large numbers of people, whose total working time is very likely many times greater than that which goes into textbooks produced in the typical manner by a single author or a small team of authors. And the supplementary materials—the laboratory programs, films, teachers' guides, and out-of-class reading materials—are quite unlike anything produced previously in this field in providing a comprehensive program of study.

The ready acceptance of these new curriculum programs in so many schools in so short a time gives a strong indication that school people generally are alert to the need to keep science teaching in the schools abreast of science itself—or, at least, to limit the gap between science and science curriculum to a few years rather than decades. The pattern of change in science teaching has apparently been set with the prospect of continuing curriculum revision being accepted as the educational status quo.

CHAPTER V

The Ninth Grade Course In Science:
A Dilemma

The developers of each of the new high school science curricula attempted to produce a one-year course which would give a reasonable sampling of the most important ideas in a particular field along with a fair understanding of the way scientists attack problems. It was clear from the outset, however, that this was virtually an impossible task. Shortly after the appearance of BSCS biology, CHEM Study and CBA chemistry, and PSSC physics, the scientists were lamenting the fact that a good deal of the important content in their disciplines had been omitted. As a result a clamor soon went up to include in the junior high school sequence some of the ideas "left over" from the high school courses, or perhaps more properly, to build a junior high school science course which would be correlated with the high school courses.

Another result of the recent activity in curriculum development has been the demand by those in scientific disciplines other than biology, chemistry, and physics to provide "equal time" for the development of the basic ideas in their fields. These people argue that there are many separate areas of science today, each recognized to be important and to stand by itself. Since the typical high school student takes only three sciences at most, it is clear that even our best prepared high school graduates have no conception of a great many important areas of science; astronomers, geologists, meteorologists, psychologists, oceanographers, and many, many others feel that their subjects should be given their day in court.

These concerns for extending and deepening the sciences already treated in high school and for adding other disciplines to an already crowded curriculum have put intense pressures on the junior high school, particularly at the ninth grade level.

Since the ninth grade is included in many American high schools, and since the ultimate disposition of the problems of curriculum at the ninth grade level will also affect those high schools where it is not, this matter would seem to be worthy of consideration in a book on modern high school science teaching. In this chapter, then, we shall explore some of the proposals for the ninth grade science course. Their rationale will be described along with their historical backgrounds where they apply.

Earth Science as a Ninth Grade Subject

Though opinion as to degree varies greatly, it is probably safe to say that those concerned with the teaching of science are in near unanimous agreement that the range of scientific subject matter offered in high school should be increased. Virtually every authority objects to the deficiencies created by limiting formal science offerings to biology, chemistry, and physics. It is nevertheless plain that the schools cannot include a large number of additional courses in an already bulging curriculum. The question is which of the "other sciences" should be added, how, and where in the curriculum should they appear?

Probably the most widely discussed subject area is earth science. An intensive effort has recently been mounted to find a place in the public school science sequence for a course dealing with the makeup of the earth and its atmosphere and the relationship of the earth to other bodies in our solar system. Several groups are now developing materials along these lines and, without doubt, the earth sciences will claim a much more prominent role in the science curriculum than is presently the case. Perhaps the most commonly discussed proposal calls for offering a course in earth science in the ninth grade.

To many, the idea of including a solid course in earth science at the pre-college level seems too new and too radical to be appealing. In reality, however, this proposal is an attempt to re-introduce a subject formerly given considerable attention. In fact the majority of American high schools at the turn of the century offered courses dealing with the earth on an equal basis with the more familiar high school science subjects. The typical high school at that time encompassed four years and the student normally took ninth grade physiography, geology, or physical geography; tenth grade biology; eleventh grade chemistry, and twelfth grade physics. This pattern was designed to provide the student with a reasonable cross section of the sciences.

The reader is reminded that the schools of the early 1900s were designed almost exclusively for college preparatory students. This approach was reasonable since the vast majority of the students entering the high school not only intended to go to college after graduation but, coming from the upper stratum socially, economically, and intellectually, were able to do so.

Early in the century the change in educational philosophy resulted in large numbers of students in the high schools who had no such aspirations or abilities. The students who formed the vanguard of this invasion, naturally enough, found it quite difficult to cope with courses which had been designed for a relatively elite population. This, in essence, meant that considerable attention had to be directed to the development of courses which were geared more closely to the needs of the new high school population.

One of the results of this concern for non college-bound students had far reaching effects. For a variety of reasons, large numbers of the lower ability students dropped out of school at the end of the eighth year of elementary school. The attempt to stimulate students to stay in school longer, coupled with the pressures for additional classroom space created by the increasing numbers of the students entering the schools, led to the creation of a unique educational institution, the junior high school. In essence, it was reasoned that students who dropped out of school at the end of the eighth grade in the old program would remain at least through the ninth grade in a pattern encompassing a six year elementary school, a three year junior high school, and a three year senior high school.

A major consequence for our purposes of the development of the junior high school was that the ninth grade course in earth science found a home in this new institution. Since the elementary schools of the day included very little science and the junior high schools were not immediately prepared to develop new curricula, those students who dropped out of school at the ninth grade received as their only exposure to science the course in earth science.

Beginning about 1910, a vigorous attempt was made to provide a broader science background for public school students. The opponents of the existing plan proposed a course dealing with a wider variety of science topics that would give a broader exposure to science to the students who would leave school at the end of the ninth grade. A lengthy controversy raged between the proponents of the ninth grade physical geography course and those who advocated the more general ninth grade course, to be called general science. In the debate the physical geographers countered the argument against limited exposure to science by claiming that there is no such thing as "general science," that such a course would become a collection of isolated topics giving the student no real understanding of science.

Despite the arguments of the physical geographers, by 1925 the battle was over and a course in general science had been substituted for the one in earth science. Within a short time increased science offerings were extended to all grades in the junior high school; with this step, general science became the heart of the entire junior high school science sequence. Thus the total pattern soon became general science in grades seven, eight, and nine; biology in grade ten; chemistry in grade eleven, and physics in grade twelve. This pattern has not changed significantly.

Despite the general demise of earth science as a public school subject, a few school systems retained the course as part of the junior high school program. This practice was almost entirely confined to the eastern states, most notably to New York State. The courses were widely scattered, however, and involved relatively few students.

In the late 1940s a revival of the earth sciences began in New York State. Shortly after World War II the New York State Education Department began to encourage the teaching of earth science in the junior high school, especially for accelerated students, generally at the ninth grade level. Since then the enrollment in earth science in New York has steadily climbed to its present level which is estimated at 45,000 students (1963–64).

Although the rebirth of earth science can generally be traced to the New York State effort, the growth of a similar course in Pennsylvania has been even more dramatic. In 1958 the Pennsylvania State Department of Public Instruction published "The Pennsylvania Guide for Teaching Earth and Space Science." This document, which served as the prototype for many publications in other states and for several commercial textbooks, served as the guide for a large-scale introduction of earth science, mostly at the ninth grade level. Earth science enrollment in Pennsylvania has steadily climbed since 1958 to its present level of some 65,000 students. Other states making significant efforts to revive the teaching of earth science include New Jersey, Illinois, and California.

The Nature of Earth Science

It is quite clear, then, that there is a major trend toward including more of what has generally been called earth science in the curriculum. But what should be included in such a course? Or, even more fundamentally, just what is "earth science" and what are the structural threads which might be used to tie such a course together? These questions are more difficult to answer for earth science than for perhaps any other subject so far discussed. Physics and chemistry have existed as discrete subjects for over one hundred years in the United States and most chemists and physicists have some idea of what a course in these subjects should consist. Although the history of biology as a school subject is much shorter, the meshing of the several sub-sciences which comprise it came about almost thirty years ago and is now generally accepted.

In the earth sciences the situation is entirely different. Earth science is usually defined as some combination of geology, astronomy, meteorology, oceanography, and perhaps even cosmology. These subjects are normally taught as separate courses at the college level and most "earth scientists" are specialists in one of these fields. Since they are taught as single subjects and very little attention has ever been given to identifying the common threads which run through all of them, the development of a good unified earth science course is difficult. There is always danger that the course will develop into four or five rather unrelated sub-courses in the several sub-sciences. In addition some of the standards given in Chapter I are difficult to apply to the course in earth science. The two salient features of modern science teaching were identified as follows:

> 1. The students should be actively involved in activities similar to those to which the scientists devote themselves. They should discover for themselves the major generalizations.
> 2. The content of the courses should represent fundamental science—it should be built around the basic principles of the discipline.

When one ponders the fact that earth science is composed of several sub-sciences, the difficulties in attempting to have students discover the major generalizations become apparent. A student in

Colorado, for example, may read about the important generalizations of oceanography but he certainly will not have the opportunity to work first hand with the ocean as his laboratory. The problem is the same for the student in Florida who is studying mountain building. In short, no place in the United States is sufficiently varied from the earth science viewpoint to allow direct study of any reasonable portion of the important ideas in that field.

Any attempt to identify the "basics" of earth science reveals another serious problem: neither earth science collectively nor the sub-sciences which make it up are really "basic." The major generalizations in these fields are essentially applications of mathematics, physics, and chemistry to a specific class of phenomena. A list of the "fundamental principles" of earth science is likely to consist essentially of some of the basic laws of chemistry and physics.

Attention is called to the work of the Earth Science Curriculum Project (ESCP). This group, established in 1962 by the American Geological Institute, is actively working to produce an earth science course for ninth grade students. In the fall of 1964 they published preliminary editions of a textbook, a teacher's guide, and a laboratory manual. Since these materials are scheduled to undergo serious revision following tryout in the schools, we will not deal in detail with them but will rather consider the plans and purposes of the ESCP group.

As one of their earliest efforts, the group attempted to unify the major themes which would be used to unify the text materials, with the following results:

1. *Science as inquiry.* Experimentation and intuition are important in the earth sciences, but ultimately, observation of nature is the true basis of all knowledge.

2. *Universality of change.* The earth is a dynamic planet; nothing about it is static, nothing really endures.

3. *Flow of energy.* Universality of change in earth materials is a consequence of the redistribution of energy, and the "running down" of the energy level of the system.

4. *Adaptation to environmental change.* The goal is equilibrium, a state of balance between opposing forces in an environment.

5. *Conservation of mass and energy.* The processes and changes observable on the earth obey all the basic laws of the physical universe.

6. *Significance of components and their relationships in space*

and time. Understanding any aspect of the earth requires consideration of the physical and chemical nature of the components and their relationships in space and time.

7. *Uniformitarianism.* The past can be interpreted only if one understands the present.

8. *Comprehension of scale.* Earth scientists must think to scale, although illustrations of natural phenomena usually involve enlargement or reduction.

9. *Prediction.* Prediction of future events, processes, and relationships is a goal of most scientific inquiries.

10. *Presentation.* Presentation of principles and concepts should reflect the historical development of earth science.[1]

When one compares these statements with the statements of themes and objectives of the groups who produced the new courses in physics and chemistry, one notes a strong similarity. Those who seek to develop curriculum materials for earth science will have serious problems in finding distinctive themes around which to build the course.

The difficulties in organizing the subject matter and the necessary prerequisites in mathematics and the physical sciences combine to present special problems for the curriculum developer. First, almost necessarily, such a course will deal heavily in models, maps, and other forms of vicarious experience. Furthermore, since earth science, if offered at the ninth grade level, precedes any serious treatment of the physical sciences, it must be highly inter-disciplinary in nature, and it must include whatever knowledge of physical science the student will need.

These difficulties are being met in several ways. Sometimes the need for physical science is simply ignored. Most of the standard textbooks written in the past fifteen years have played down the role of the physical sciences in earth science. The emphasis in these books has been on phenomenon rather than upon cause. In traditional treatments of mountain building, for example, this phenomenon is generally treated as a "wrinkling of the earth's crust," some sort of "volcanic activity," or simply the movement of one side of a "crack in the earth" riding up above the other side. In such discussions very little attention is normally given to the basic principles of force as physical phenomena which apply to mountain building.

---

[1] *ESCP Newsletter,* NL-1, October, 1963, Earth Science Curriculum Project, Boulder, Colorado, p. 3.

The ESCP group seems to be taking the opposite approach. Although the ESCP textbooks and laboratory manuals do not dwell at length on the physical principles needed, no attempt is made to avoid using physical science to explain earth science phenomenon. The approach in this course to situations which call for the use of physical science principles is to state the principle (or to refer the student to the appendix where a compilation of many important physical science generalizations is to be found) and then show the application of this principle to the particular situation being discussed.

A second group concerned with the development of earth science materials takes a somewhat different approach. The developers of the new course entitled "Time, Space, and Matter"[2] use the earth as their basic subject matter but make no attempt to teach earth science *per se*. The course might be considered a distinctly interdisciplinary treatment of the physics and chemistry of the earth. Large areas of what is commonly identified as earth science are left completely untouched, but a reasonably complete treatment of selected topics is achieved.

In the matter of providing direct student activities, there are also several different approaches. Traditional earth science textbooks have tended to rely rather heavily upon rock and mineral specimens, motion pictures, slides, pictures, maps, and charts. Beyond this, no attempt is generally made to provide direct student experience, as the authors are inclined to use textbook descriptions to convey the ideas intended.

The ESCP group utilizes all of the devices listed above plus an abundance of models. In one case, the student studies the relationship between the rate of flow of a stream and the rate of erosion by constructing a model of a stream in the classroom using the water faucet as the source of the stream.

The "Time, Space, and Matter" course, since it involves essentially the physics and chemistry of the earth, deals heavily in basic physics and chemistry experiments. One of the important topics is the fundamental characteristics of matter in the liquid, solid, and gaseous states. The experiments for this part of the course deal with the general phenomenon rather than its application to a specific

---

[2] F. L. Ferris, Jr., ed., *Time, Space, and Matter,* Junior High School Science Project (Princeton, N.J.: Princeton University, 1964).

geological situation. Thus the experiments can be done with ordinary chemical glassware and reagents.

Although there are many problems yet to be solved in the teaching of earth science and no real pattern for the course has yet emerged, the indications are clear that this subject will become more common in the ninth grade. But because of the difficulties involved, it is by no means clear that earth science will become *the* ninth grade science subject. What then, are some of the other possibilities?

Biology as a Ninth Grade Subject

One of the most important lessons we have learned from the current ferment in science education is that students are able to learn science concepts and processes much earlier in life than was previously thought to be the case. A tempting interpretation of this generalization is to suggest that the entire high school science sequence should be moved one grade forward, or, in other words, that biology should be offered in the ninth grade, chemistry in the tenth grade, and physics in the eleventh grade.

Such a suggestion leads, of course, to the question of what should be offered in the twelfth grade. Two answers are commonly given: several authorities suggest offering an advanced course in biology, chemistry, or physics thereby doubling the student's exposure to one of the sciences. A second proposal is to develop a research course or advanced seminar in which the students do considerable independent study. Occasionally it is proposed that the twelfth grade be devoted to a course in earth science. There is presently no perceptible trend in this direction, however.

Regardless of what is offered in the twelfth grade, the suggestion that the student's progress through the science sequence be accelerated has led a number of school systems to offer biology in the ninth grade. Most of these experiments are based on the assumption that ninth grade students are capable of dealing with the existing courses. Several school systems are now experimenting with both traditional and BSCS biology as ninth grade courses.

The science education community is generally divided into two camps with respect to ninth grade biology. The proponents argue that such a program allows the bright children to move ahead more rapidly. They also argue that children in the ninth grade are at an age when they are genuinely interested in living things and especially in their own developing bodies, and are therefore more amenable to biology instruction than they would be a year later.

The other side protests that the movement is a dangerous trend and that little will be gained by such a change. Their argument runs as follows: biology is a science which is based upon chemistry, physics, and mathematics, as well as on certain basic notions of its own; if a student is to comprehend biological science, he must have a good background in the supporting sciences. (As a matter of fact, these same people frequently suggest that the biology course be given in the twelfth grade to be preceded by courses in chemistry and physics.) Those who object to the ninth grade course point out that the development of the more difficult BSCS course (and other courses which are now appearing) necessitates that students be given as long as possible to mature mentally and physically and to gain a good background in the other sciences before taking biology.

The inconclusiveness of the research on this subject means that the school systems which have decided either for or against an accelerated science sequence, including a ninth grade course in biology, have done so largely on an intuitive basis. There does not now appear to be a national trend toward ninth grade biology, although the schools in certain regions, most notably the Midwest, do show a perceptible trend in this direction.

Physical Science as a Ninth Grade Subject

One of the major points developed in the earlier discussion of the nature of modern biological science was that the study of biology today demands a certain background in physics and chemistry. Much of the study of biology is essentially a consideration of basic physical and chemical phenomena with respect to that certain type of matter which we have collectively called life. This means that the developers of the BSCS biology course and other modern courses are faced with the problem of how to properly convey the concepts of the physical sciences to the study of biology.

This problem was solved by the BSCS writers by including a relatively heavy dose of physical science in the early chapters of their books. An examination of the Blue Version of the BSCS course makes it clear that, although the chapter headings all sound like biology, the content of much of the first half of the book is basic physical science.

Although there appears to be general agreement that the BSCS course probably does a good job of presenting physical science to the biology student, not everyone is satisfied with the situation. Many biologists now see the need for a course in basic physical science to be offered at the junior high school level that would, hopefully, do a more thorough and systematic job of treating this content. The biology teachers could then move more quickly into the subject matter in which they are primarily interested.

A somewhat similar situation exists with respect to high school chemistry and physics. The developers of the PSSC physics course made it clear at the outset that they would make no attempt to "cover" physics. Rather, they set out to deal with the most fundamental concepts they could identify. This means that many topics which physicists consider to be important are dealt with very briefly, if at all. There are two important reasons for this situation. First, the emphasis on basic principles necessitated the elimination of many practical topics: for example, the usual study of electric circuits and simple machines. Second, the painstaking attention to fundamental physics has made it necessary to reduce the number of topics. To some it may seem that the course ends at the point where the students have learned just enough to begin to profit from their study of physics—which means from the practical applications of physics to engineering and technology. Many physicists argue that a course taught at the junior high school level dealing with some of the elementary concepts of physics and certain practical applications to the world around him would prepare the student for a better course in high school. And although the subject matter differs, a strikingly similar situation could be described for chemistry.

The most significant effort to produce an integrated physical science course for the ninth grade has been undertaken by a group at Educational Services Incorporated under the direction of Professor Uri Haber-Schaim, who was one of the developers of the PSSC course. Large-scale testing in schools was begun in the fall of 1965 following more than two years of work by Dr. Haber-Schaim and his associates, during which the materials were tried out with pilot classes. A preliminary version consisting of eleven chapters of combined text-laboratory guide material was printed in the summer of

1965, with the final hard cover book, entitled *Introductory Physical Science* (IPS),[3] ready for release in 1966.

The course has as its central theme the development of evidence for an atomic model of matter. It is concerned with the properties of matter, with the characteristics which give rise to the differences and similarities among objects, and it involves the student in an investigation of the properties of matter than he can observe and measure.

Like most of the new curricula in science, IPS follows a well-defined path toward the major objective and is not just a broad survey of physical science. The method is that of student experimentation and guided reasoning in analyzing the results. The authors have placed the laboratory experiments and the text together in such a way that, as he reads the book, the student views an experiment as something he must do to obtain the information necessary to understand an idea or concept. The course could not exist without the laboratory experiments since many of the conclusions and generalizations which result from the experiments become essential parts of the text. Special efforts have been made to include experiments which can be done in schools without science laboratories. The equipment for the IPS experiments is relatively simple and inexpensive and they can be performed on individual flat desk tops.

IPS recognizes the need for an experimental science course to precede those which typically come in the tenth, eleventh, and twelfth grades. Their course relies heavily on the experimental approach to the study of science employed in PSSC physics, CHEM Study, and CBA chemistry, and is therefore regarded as an especially appropriate experience for those who will take laboratory-centered courses in high school. But it should also serve as a useful course for those who will not study science further for, after all, it deals with some of the most fundamental ideas in the physical world —ideas which should be useful in helping the child understand natural events and phenomena in the world around him. For example, the student makes careful measurements of many of the basic properties of matter, such as volume, mass, density, expansion, elasticity, freezing and melting points, solubility. He is chiefly concerned about what these properties of substances tell him about matter's behavior in other ways, and how he can use his observations

---

[3] *Introductory Physical Science,* Preliminary Edition (Watertown, Mass.: Physical Science Study Committee of Educational Services Inc., 1964).

and the generalizations to which they lead to gain a better understanding of the similarities and differences among objects.

In summary then, there are a number of good reasons for developing a course in physical science for the junior high school, preferably the ninth grade. The major arguments are that it would come before biology, chemistry, and physics in the high school and would serve to provide the needed prerequisite training for those courses; and, that by the ninth grade the students should have gained sufficient maturity and mathematical facility to handle the quantitative ideas to be developed.

CHAPTER VI

Needed: A Modern Teacher
For Modern Science

Probably the most important and the most enduring consequence of the new curriculum projects in science has been the pattern they established for attacking the problems of education. The public, at last, came to understand that broader support for the improvement of education was essential. Our system of education has had built into it various devices, the purposes of which, it seemed, were to prevent change, never to promote it. But now, with the concern shown by the scholars and under the pressure of international events following Sputnik I in October, 1957, the public mood changed and it became acceptable to use tax monies for the betterment of education. Events since then indicate vastly increased interest in education by the people and, especially, by the government. The history of these events will show that the precedents of PSSC physics and the others gave the budding movement much of the momentum which carried it forward to the Elementary and Secondary Education Act of 1965, a landmark in the public support of education.

The summer and in-service institutes funded by the National Science Foundation, the pattern of field testing leading to multiple revisions by the original authors after they had examined the feedback from schools, the follow-up activities which provide continuing opportunities for teachers to keep the writers informed on day-to-day classroom problems (ESI still conducts PSSC Area Meetings for physics teachers throughout the country for this purpose)—all of these elements in the science curriculum projects have had a great influence on the evolution of education in this country.

The efforts of the PSSC physics group and those who have done similar work in related areas have brought about what might be called the Mid-Century Revolution in American Education. There have already been major changes in education, especially in the sciences and mathematics in the high schools. The curricula have been altered to reflect new knowledge and an immensely improved organization of traditional topics as well. Education, in short, has taken a giant leap forward.

Although the course-content improvement projects center on improvement in curriculum, in the "what" of learning, another aspect of the question soon appeared. Some attention must be paid to the "how" of learning, to the performance of the teacher in the classroom and laboratory. The teacher-education issue has now been raised in such a way that it can no longer be ignored. For the new curricula, on which large amounts of human and material resources have been spent, will never be completely effective until all the classrooms are staffed with fully competent instructors. The goals of the new courses, however noble, and the materials for teaching and learning, however carefully structured, will never be fully implemented until the vast number of our teachers understand something of the philosophy that has been so carefully woven into the fabric of the new curricula.

The resources of men and money should now be directed toward improving the quality and process of teacher education. One can already detect some hopeful signs of activity in this area. These include the concern expressed by the Commission on Science Education of the American Association for the Advancement of Science and the appointment by Chairman Paul Sears of a sub-committee to consider the commission's responsibilities in this field; the stirrings at a number of colleges and universities, admittedly a small number as yet, for improvements in both content and education courses for teachers; and the serious interest on the part of Educational Services Incorporated which has already led to the establishment of experimental programs for teachers and for teachers of teachers. There are no doubt other individuals and groups whose work has not yet become widely known.

One wonders about the approaches that the different programs will take. The possibilities seem almost endless, and if the ideas now being discussed can be taken as an indication, a great variety of experimental programs will be tried. One thing seems certain: some of the philosophy and, indeed, some of the practices from the new curricula in science and mathematics will surely be reflected in the teacher education efforts. Those elements of philosophy and practice will have applications that extend far beyond the curriculum areas they started out to reform.

Teaching the New Science

An examination of a textbook developed for use with any of the new secondary school science curricula makes it clear that the developers of the new curricula were aiming for quite different kinds of understandings from those which our high school courses have traditionally called for. Earlier chapters have dealt with some of the salient points of difference. Naturally one would expect the students in such different types of programs to perform quite differently, yet surprisingly, such differences in students' performances have proved very difficult to detect with the kinds of tests now in use. (This question is discussed at length in Chapter VII.) Many people are concerned as to just why the differences that we "know" are present cannot be more easily demonstrated.

There are, of course, many facets of this question which might be explored. Without doubt such questions as the limitations of present-day evaluative instruments, the usual difficulties of educational measurement, and the others to be discussed in Chapter VII are relevant. There is one factor, however, which perhaps overrides all others, not only from the point of view of the differences which should be expected in students, but more importantly, in terms of the success or failure of the curricular innovations in science. This is the problem of who teaches the science and how it is taught. Although new kinds of textbooks, carefully contrived educational films, and unique laboratory experiences are important elements in the science program, the science teacher still serves as the interpreter of these things to the student and is at the center of the teaching-learning situation. Only if his interpretation reflects the philosophy of the course developers is it reasonable to say that the student has "taken" the new course. If it differs sharply from the philosophy which guided the developers, one can say only that the student has enrolled for a given course—and perhaps received credit for it. He may well not have learned what the textbook and other aids to learning were intended to help him learn.

Thus one hypothesis put forth to explain the unexpectedly small differences which have been detected in students in the new courses in science and students in traditional courses is that some of those who purport to teach the new courses actually do not do so at all. Much of the difficulty which some teachers experience in translating the new programs into effective classroom instruction can be traced directly to the kinds of teacher training programs which they have undergone. Few present-day science teachers receive as part of their education for teaching the kind of experience which the new programs call for. Unless appropriate patterns can be developed for the retraining of the existing corps of teachers, and more importantly, for the training of a new generation of teachers, the present curriculum efforts and any which are attempted in the future will fall far short of their potential.

Teaching science has always been a difficult job and today it is far more difficult than it ever has been in the past. Today's science teacher must have a thorough mastery of the subject matter he will teach, he must understand the nature of the learning process, and he must have a broad general education. Of course, many people lacking these qualifications are assigned to teach science, because it is virtually impossible to carry on without them.

Fifty years ago the education of the science teacher was a fairly simple matter. It centered on the mastery of the subject he was to teach, with very little attention being given to the psychology of learning or to other matters relating to the interaction of teacher and learner. When the school's central purpose was to serve the needs of those who were to go to college, the problems of teaching were far less complex. Students were automatically grouped homogeneously, which simplified much of teaching. With the change in emphasis in the modern school where the goal is to provide the best possible education for all students of all ranges of abilities, the variability in learners coupled with problems of evaluation, the proper selection of teaching materials, and similar matters, have become infinitely more complex. Sidney Hood described the situation well when he said, "If one feels a responsibility only to a subject or to a discipline, teaching is the easiest activity in the world, especially if one enjoys monologue. But if one also feels a responsibility to the student, to each student, teaching is difficult."

The education of a science teacher should be thought of as a continuous process extending from the undergraduate experience in college through the professional career of the teacher. While prospective science teachers and those who are already in the classrooms differ in approach to the study of many professional problems, there should nonetheless be no sharp distinction between pre-service and in-service education. Both are designed to encourage the growth of the teacher of modern science and to make him a more effective professional person.

This chapter is devoted to an analysis of the general problems of science teacher education; more specifically it considers the kind of teacher education which the new curricula calls for; and it suggests how training programs for present and future science teachers might be organized.

Undergraduate Education

A casual reading of the earlier chapters on biology, chemistry, physics, and earth science teaching could conceivably lead to a conclusion which was not intended. These chapters emphasize the need of all students, regardless of vocational aims, for an understanding of science in some depth. This leads logically, and intentionally, to the idea that the science teacher must have substantial training in science. What was not intended was the idea that all—or nearly all —of the courses in science teacher education programs should be courses in pure science.

The undergraduate education of prospective science teachers may be divided into three phases. The student must have, first of all, a good general education background. As a teacher, his first qualification should be that of an educated person. He must know how to speak the language and to write it. He should understand something of the economics of the world in which he lives, as well as its history and geography. It would be highly desirable for him to have command of a second language. Reuben Gustavson, in addressing the U.S. Office of Education's 1958 Conference on Mathematics and Science Education in the U.S. Public Schools, made a strong plea for a liberal program of general education for science and mathematics teachers. He said:

> The study of the humanities must go hand in hand with the study of mathematics and science. In today's world, as always, we must make value judgments based on conceptions of right and wrong, of justice and injustice, of the liberty and dignity of man. Where will we find help in making value judgments as a basis for our actions? Not in

science because science is not concerned with value judgments. In the humanities, yes—in the study of religion, philosophy, history, and literature.[1]

In many colleges and universities, the general education or basic studies phase of the student's undergraduate program amounts to one-third or more of the total program. This is probably a reasonable figure. If the courses give a good representation of the important areas of a liberal education, and if they are well taught by instructors who understand and appreciate the values of general education and who do not consider such teaching assignments to be a necessary evil to be endured for the privilege of carrying out research or teaching more specialized courses, then general education may indeed help people make value judgments and carry out more adequately the role of responsible citizenship.

The second necessity in the pre-service program is that which deals with the subject matter training of the prospective teacher. Here, perhaps more than in any other area, the teacher training institutions have failed most seriously to do an adequate job. Shallowness in science training is probably the most serious limiting factor with respect to the teaching of the new science courses.

In matters of science, the science teacher must first of all be a scientist who can hold up his head with others in the scientific community. He must have studied his subject thoroughly enough that he can be described as reasonably expert in it. Probably he should have had the equivalent of an undergraduate major in one of the science areas plus a minor in a second, preferably closely related, such as physics and mathematics, or physics and chemistry.

It is not enough, however, that the prospective science teacher take the proper number of science courses. He must also receive the right kind of science courses. It is axiomatic that one teaches as he was taught. Unless the college science courses are philosophically "in tune" with the kind of science which the prospective teacher will be expected to deal with in his own teaching, there is a serious question as to whether he will be able to cope successfully with the problems of teaching modern science.

The design of science courses for prospective teachers, as well as for those in other fields, rests perhaps more heavily upon teaching

---

[1] *Mathematics and Science in U.S. Public Schools,* Circular 533 (Washington: U.S. Office of Education, 1958), p. 2.

style than upon anything else. The content of a college science course is likely to be appropriate if it is selected by a man competent in his subject. If, however, the content is developed as a series of lectures emphasizing what is known in science, it is not likely to be completely appropriate. The prospective science teacher must take laboratory-centered courses which emphasize how present scientific knowledge was arrived at. If he does not receive this type of training in his own courses, he can scarcely be expected to pass these ideas along to his students.

When considering the content of science courses for the prospective teacher, it must be remembered, however, that there is a need for breadth of training as well as depth if he is to function in the complex role which the modern high school demands. It is a fact of life in the American high school that the science teacher usually does not teach a single subject but is required to teach in two or more branches of science. In addition, he is often called upon to be the director of a science club or to work with students in preparing science fair projects or in a number of other ways which demand a knowledge in at least two fields of science.

The third phase of the teacher's pre-service education is that which is commonly called "professional education." For reasons already stated, the good science teacher must be skilled in testing and evaluating and should have a knowledge of the principles of guidance necessary to carry on an adequate program of classroom counseling. He must know something of human development and learning, and of the recent studies in that field.

The prospective teacher should have some insight into the history and philosophy of education so that he can place the modern high school in perspective. He should also understand and appreciate the total school curriculum and its purposes, and in particular should see the relationship between science and the other high school subjects. Finally, he must be familiar with the most recent tools to make his job more effective. Such things as the latest audio-visual equipment, techniques of educational television and programmed instruction, and recent developments in laboratory equipment must be included in his education. The latter are particularly important in view of the highly laboratory-centered science programs of today.

Although there is considerable variation in the relative emphases given these three phases of teacher education in different institutions, many American universities now require the prospective science teacher to take forty to fifty semester hours in general education, sixty or more in science and mathematics content, and about twenty semester hours in professional education, generally including an internship or practice teaching period. It is plain that a student in such an institution has little time left for electives in a four-year program. In fact, some students preparing to become science teachers find it impossible to complete this sequence in four years even if they take no electives.

Prospective science teachers have a special problem in this regard since their education, more than that of teachers of other subjects, must be broad. It must include work in two or more branches of science along with the necessary courses in mathematics. Increasingly, the five-year program is seen to be the answer to this problem even in states which do not require five years for permanent certification of all high school teachers.

The five-year, or equivalent, preparation program for secondary-school teachers is one of the more significant changes now taking place in teacher education. Some universities award master's degrees at the end of the program, while others require additional work for it. In either case, many school systems award salary increases for the fifth year of work whether or not a degree has been earned by it.

Graduate Education

Graduate degrees loom ever larger in the professional life of the science teacher. There is first of all the need for the science teacher to continue his studies in order to stay abreast of the rapid changes in science. In addition, he is, like others, concerned with the increases in salary which come with the acquisition of advanced degrees.

Our approaches to graduate education in the past have not produced the kind of results which should be expected. A serious problem lies in the practice of teachers in all fields of taking graduate work in school administration and other areas unrelated to their teaching fields. This practice has been prompted by hoped-for employment in school administration or supervision with the improved salaries that generally accompany those positions, and also by the fact that most colleges and universities offer graduate courses in professional education more freely than they do in science. This practice is an unfortunate one on two counts: although courses in administration and supervision are of value for the school administrator, the science teacher's performance is enhanced very little by taking such courses; and second, a small percentage of those who take advanced work in school administration ever become school administrators.

Because the field of science is changing more rapidly than any other area, the practice of science teachers taking graduate work which is unrelated to the teaching of science is perhaps more unfortunate than is the comparable situation in, say, mathematics, English, or foreign languages. Rather strong objections have been raised to this practice recently. California and Florida have already enacted legislation which makes it relatively unprofitable to obtain a degree which does not have immediate application to one's teaching field. In addition, many local school districts throughout the country have adopted similar regulations.

Assuming then that the graduate education of a science teacher should be related to science teaching, what kinds of courses should he take? The more forward-looking graduate programs in science education require the student to take work in both professional education and in science with something like half of the work being taken in each area. Such programs are based on the belief that, to become more proficient in his teaching, the science teacher should have additional work in professional education, especially in educational measurement and methods and materials of teaching science. Some of the graduate science methods courses are now giving special emphasis to the new secondary school curriculum developments, thereby making the transition in the classroom to these programs easier.

The graduate work in science itself should emphasize recent discoveries and concepts. The distinguishing feature of the graduate work in the best modern graduate programs in science education is their flexibility. Thus there is opportunity to add training in areas which could not be given adequate attention in the undergraduate program. In some institutions, the graduate student is permitted to take what is normally considered undergraduate work, generally with additional assignments.

The need for study in depth in a particular branch of science is now a serious problem for science teachers and it will likely become more so. Teachers whose undergraduate education reflects the "broad science fields" approach (a little work in all of the sciences and very little depth in any one) face the problem of inadequate preparation for respectable graduate level science courses. This problem is especially acute in the physical sciences where nearly all graduate level courses require advanced mathematics. A few years ago the courses which a great many of today's science teachers studied as undergraduates stressed an approach to science which was far more descriptive and less quantitative than that which most science departments demand today.

A critical situation exists at the advanced graduate level in science education. Only a handful of doctoral degrees in science education are awarded annually. At this moment, in the face of the great need for leadership in the development of new curriculum materials and special measures for the science education of both the gifted and the slow learner, and when research in the teaching and learning of science is desperately needed, the profession has a responsibility to encourage its most promising young people to pursue doctoral degrees. In the period ahead when science education must extend itself to keep pace with the revolution in science itself, dynamic leadership will be in great demand.

In-Service Education

There is another major problem in science teacher education which goes beyond the matter of degree programs. Not long ago almost every science teacher in the United States, regardless of what degrees he held, was in serious need of help in his understanding of science. While the situation regarding in-service education is less serious today, it still must be considered a major educational problem. Probably the major gains which have been made stem from a rather intensive effort by the federal government in this regard: in 1950 the national government, recognizing its role in the promotion of various aspects of science in the national welfare, established the National Science Foundation. In addition to providing encouragement and financial support for research and development in all branches of science, the Foundation, through its Division of Scientific Personnel and Education, has been actively involved in the improvement of science teaching in the public schools. Several programs of assistance to high school science and mathematics teachers have been developed and they are of special interest here. In particular, the summer and in-service institutes operated by the colleges and universities in the United States and financed by the National Science Foundation have had a major impact on science education in America.

For the past several years, a sizeable percentage of the nation's high school science teachers have attended institutes supported by the NSF. By far the most popular have been the summer institutes. Since the early 1960s, in excess of 20,000 science and mathematics teachers each year have been granted awards for summer study at colleges and universities, most of which have developed special instructional programs designed to meet the particular needs of those in attendance. In most cases, such institutes are organized and staffed by the faculties of the various science departments. Often this has been the scientists' first opportunity to express their interest in the education of teachers. Their participation has helped to bring about a major change in science education. Scientists in increasing numbers have been learning first hand of the problems of public school teachers and many have been prompted to visit the schools and otherwise to acquaint themselves with their problems as they have never done before.

The in-service institute typically serves the teachers in a limited geographical area. These teachers travel to a nearby college or university for evening or Saturday classes which run throughout the academic year. These have been most common and perhaps most successful in metropolitan areas where it is possible for the teachers to meet for Saturday morning or evening classes at a centrally located higher education institution—although in some cases the college or university chooses to have the classes meet in a high school.

Of special interest among NSF-supported institutes are the programs dealing with the new secondary school science curriculum projects, which have been offered by many colleges and universities since the late 1950s. These have made it possible for participating teachers to introduce the new courses to their students by receiving help each week from a professor of science in matters related specifically to the new courses. The special value of in-service institutes in this regard comes from the immediacy of the teaching-learning situation: when a teacher has the opportunity to bring to his weekly in-service class problems which his students have presented within the past few days, he is able to get from his science instructor and perhaps from his fellow teachers who may be facing similar problems, a kind of help which is uniquely valuable. The learning situation is highly specific—a great contrast with the vague, general character of many in-service courses. There can be no doubt that the motivation for the teacher to learn is unusually high in this situation and his effectiveness in transmitting the new knowledge to his students may likewise be unusually high.

But why have the NSF programs been so successful when various types of "extension" courses offered in the past, according to many teachers, have not been? There is an important difference between the NSF-supported institute and the extension course: financial support for the teacher. In NSF programs, tuition for the teacher is waived and the expenses of textbooks and travel to and from the class meetings are underwritten. In the case of summer institutes, the teacher receives a stipend to cover his living expenses and those of his family for the period of the institute. Many teachers in the past have found it difficult if not impossible from a financial standpoint to obtain the in-service training so badly needed. The support of the National Science Foundation has helped to resolve this problem.

The NSF-supported institutes have also been the means by which science teachers have been able to obtain advanced degrees, although in some cases the colleges and universities have simply given courses without establishing degree programs. The NSF has recently encouraged institutions of higher education to consider more carefully the matter of degree programs and, in this way, has recognized a fact of educational life in the public schools. Salaries are tied to advanced degrees and teachers must be helped to obtain them.

Certification Requirements

An examination of certification requirements in the various states indicates that over one half either have recently adopted new requirements or are planning to do so. Present trends indicate that many states in the near future will require sixty to seventy-five semester hours of credit in science for the teacher who wishes to teach all of the high school sciences. Many states are no longer issuing certificates covering the "broad area of science" but instead are giving certification in each field separately with an individual requirement of some twenty to thirty semester hours. Many colleges and universities have modified their requirements for science teachers in line with the new certification requirements. A great many institutions have set their requirements higher than those called for by the state.

Although the more demanding certification requirements will undoubtedly result in a better prepared science teaching profession in the near future, this will not solve the problem entirely. There will not be enough teachers in the foreseeable future who qualify for certification in science to fill the vacancies in the schools of the United States. Presently there are many people in science teaching who do not meet even today's most modest requirements. There are, in fact, people teaching science in some states who do not hold a valid teaching credential, but are appointed by boards of education which insist that they cannot find qualified and certificated teachers.

Some attention is currently being given to the question of the proper status in the profession of the non-certificated teacher. It has been suggested that those who no not qualify for certification as teachers should under no circumstances be permitted to teach. It has also been proposed that those who wish to teach science but lack certification might be employed as teacher's helpers who could assist with laboratories, score papers, and do other helpful tasks in the classroom and laboratory, but might not be permitted to instruct students. Such helpers would be paid on a different salary scale, receiving considerably less than the salary paid to the certificated teacher. Such personnel would not be permitted to join professional organizations and would otherwise not be recognized as members in full standing of the teaching profession.

While such a step would doubtless deny some schools the opportunity to offer courses in science—this in view of the considerable number of schools which find it necessary to employ non-certificated teachers—it might in the end have beneficial results. It would surely focus attention on the problem of the poorly qualified science teachers now employed in so many of our schools. It might also be argued that the money saved by paying the non-certificated people who would be serving as teachers' assistants might be used for the improvement of salaries of those who qualify for certification. This would undoubtedly make the professional generally more attractive.

It should be noted that while the problem of well qualified teachers is serious in all subject matter fields, it is perhaps most serious in the sciences. The demands of industry and government for technical personnel, allied with other factors, reduce the number of well qualified teachers, particularly in the physical sciences, to an alarmingly small number. Only a small fraction of those presently teaching physics in our high schools today have been trained as physics teachers or have majored in physics in college. They have come instead from other science fields and from other professions where their training has not typically been directed toward the teaching of physics. While many of these people perform satisfactorily in the classroom, the practice of accepting as teachers those whose training for the job is universally viewed as inadequate can scarcely be expected to result in high quality education.

The New Concern for Teaching

"During a period of reform, teachers sort themselves out into four groups: those who lead, those who follow, those who rest content with the status quo, and those who vigorously resist all change. Each teacher must decide which group to join."[2]

Few will deny that the teacher's role in educational change is important—and his role in changing teaching itself is vital. Changes in certification requirements, in graduate and undergraduate programs of teacher education, and in patterns of in-service education for teachers will have only a modest influence on classroom practice unless the teacher himself sees the need for change and understands the bases for the proposed reforms.

If the teacher is to be a force into educational change, those more directly responsible for education—school administrators, professors in the colleges and universities, and educational leaders generally—must take pains to see that he is acquainted at first hand with evolving practices and procedures. There has been an abundance of dialogue about the merits and demerits of the new curricula in science and mathematics. Teachers have taken positions for and against but in some cases they have spoken without the benefit of

---

[2] Paul Woodring, *Introduction to American Education* (New York: Harcourt, Brace & World, Inc., 1965), p. 67.

first-hand knowledge. If a teacher's evaluation of educational reforms is to receive the attention which his professional position ought to demand, his opinion should reflect the sober judgment of one who has tried out the new materials in his own classroom. The new curricula in science have, above all, stressed the inductive approach to learning; they have discouraged the acceptance of facts and concepts by students without experimental evidence. The teachers of these new courses in science should, therefore, be eager to look for experimental evidence to help in the evaluation of the methods by which the new courses can best be taught. And such evidence is best obtained by classroom tryout of new materials and methods.

School administrators should, therefore, willingly have their teachers become engaged in educational innovation and experiment, rather than *adopt* one of the new curriculum programs—usually with the accompanying fanfare for the benefit of members of the board of education and the school patrons. It would be well for schools to *try out* the new materials for perhaps two or three years by indicating to all interested parties that the new materials are being accepted on a strictly experimental basis, after which a judgment will be rendered. The teacher and the school would be in a much better position to be objective about the program's merits and to speak freely about its suitability for their educational purposes.

It is hoped that the first of the four groups of teachers Woodring has identified—those who lead—will increase in number. In the end sound leadership must be based on experience, but it should be the goal of responsible educational reformers to provide maximum opportunity for classroom teachers to be on the front line of experimentation and innovation and to speak with the authority which comes from personal involvement in educational reform.

Martin Mayer in his book, *The Schools,* reminds his readers that "Someone must stand responsible for what children are forced to do, and society as a whole must stand responsible for the conduct and the quality of the schools."[3]

The "someone" to whom Mayer refers has not assumed his full responsibility for the education of our children, and the result has been an increasing awareness by the general public of the problems

---

[3] Martin Mayer, *The Schools* (New York: Harper & Row, 1961), p. xii.

of the public schools, including those of teacher education. There can be no doubt that society has neglected in large measure its responsibilities to education, but there is likewise no doubt that those who care about the education of youth are now finding ways to channel their concerns to useful ends. It may not be quite fair to say that responsible citizens have ignored the problems of the schools; it is more likely that they have been unable to find ways to express their concerns, to help in the solution of the problems of education. The scholars also, with few exceptions, have found little reason to believe that their ideas would be received warmly by school people and that their attention to the problems of education would be appreciated. The breakthrough achieved in recent years through the involvement of the scholars in curriculum development has had the effect of opening the lines of communication between the people who are legally responsible for education and those outside the schools who have come to recognize their moral responsibilities for it. The schools are at the present time more receptive to the ideas and the efforts of the scholars outside the realm of professional education than they have ever been before.

The chief consequence of this change of attitude on both sides of the schoolhouse door has been the development of new curricula in the sciences and mathematics. The new materials in physics and chemistry and biology could never have come about in the old days when school matters, including curriculum, were viewed as the exclusive domain of those employed in the public schools. Now education is changing in the most fundamental ways, and the recent changes in secondary school curriculum—changes which go to the philosophical heart of education—will surely be followed by changes of equal magnitude in teacher education.

There may be some profit in identifying some of the major shortcomings in the professional preparation of teachers and in speculating on their causes.

First, the professional education courses taught to prospective teachers are often sterile experiences for the student, devoid of any real connection to the problems of the classroom. Such courses are apt to be too abstract and too general to help neophyte teachers understand either children or the art and science of teaching. If the prospective teacher is to develop an understanding of pedagogy, of teaching methods, of child psychology, of classroom management and, indeed, of the spirit of the inductive method of scientific investigation, his instruction in these matters must be vibrant and must make clear the connection between his college courses and his performance as a teacher in a science classroom. Those responsible for teacher education must consider seriously the indictment of education courses so often made by students who have taken them: they have little appeal before graduation and little use afterwards.

The teachers of teachers—both the professors of education and the scientists who teach the subject matter courses—show a serious disregard for the special needs of their students. Neither group appears to have any regular contact with high school students in the classrooms (admittedly, a few of the former group teach classes in college- or university-demonstration high schools and occasionally one of the latter group either teaches or visits classes in the schools, but the number is relatively small). Without the stimulation which first-hand classroom experience brings, the courses in pedagogy especially have an artificiality which cannot be concealed and which is deadening to students. While teachers of the science subjects may not have quite the same responsibility for matters of pedagogy as the professors of education, it would nevertheless be helpful, in terms of their understanding of how students think and of what sort of mastery of subject matter the teachers of high school students should have, for them to visit in the science classrooms occasionally.

Another serious problem of professional education is the failure of education to qualify in the minds of many as a serious subject for formal study, as a scholarly discipline. This situation is due not so much to a lack of substance in education as a subject for study, as to the failure of professors of education to inject the reality of the teaching situation into their courses—to make the abstract concrete and the general specific.

This problem is also due, at least in part, to the difficulties always present in studies which treat human behavior. The study of phenomena in the natural sciences, for example, or in mathematics is generally more satisfying for the student and more comfortable for the teacher than studies of human behavior. The principles are less subject to individual interpretation and the facts more easily explained.

Another factor in the present situation is the difficulty of carrying on research in education, the findings of which stand firm when subject to the rules by which good research is regulated. This too has to do with the nature of the behavioral sciences, but is also partly due to the failure of competent scholars in adequate numbers to enter professional education.

It may be worth noting that many of the professors of education have arrived at their present positions by virtue of successful teaching. Thus their hierarchy of values has established classroom performance as most important, with the more scholarly activity characteristic of serious research in the disciplines placed farther down the scale.

A third problem has to do with the limited contact between prospective teachers and the students in the schools. The excursions of pre-service teachers into high school science classrooms are typically reserved for the junior and senior years. This means that the courses in science, most of which precede contact with students in the schools, are not viewed in the context of learning for teaching. Teachers should have both knowledge of the disciplines and a certain maturity in the handling of knowledge so that it may be more effectively transmitted to others. The prospective teacher is often denied the opportunity to learn as a student learns, to view the acquisition of knowledge in science as an experience in living. For example, a third grader may study the behavior of earth worms while the college freshman studies the same topic in biology, but, despite the strong similarity between the subjects, the third grade child often displays an intellectual curiosity about living things, an attitude of honest inquiry, which the college student often lacks. This attitude on the part of the college student may well be a product of his failure to make any connection between his college level study of biology and the teaching-learning situation—and that, in turn, is likely a product of a program of teacher education which separates the prospective teacher and the children he will teach until much too late in his college experience.

Finally, pre-service teachers are rarely required to consider the organization of the ideas and principles of the disciplines they study; they are not forced to search for the arrangement of the parts in the organization of the whole. The science textbook often dictates all that matters in the course: the selection of topics, the sequence in which they are taken up, and the emphasis they are given. The college student is rarely required to become involved in structuring a subject for study as good teachers must do; he is not asked to help build a course in science, even a small piece of it. Thus he plays a passive role in his own education—and he is likely to do the same in the education of the students in his own classroom in later years.

It is now being proposed by responsible people in teacher education that a partial answer to the problems above must lie in the fusing of courses in the several disciplines with those in pedagogy. It is an impossible task to teach prospective teachers the philosophy and methodology of teaching students in the absence of subject matter, and to teach subject matter with no regard for the use to which it is to be put. It is difficult for the prospective teacher to understand during his college years how the responses of students to learning situations viewed in the artificial setting of the college classroom relate to the behavior of real children in real classrooms, unless the two are tied together by means of subject matter.

Stated differently, the child must be placed in the center of the learning activities of those preparing to be teachers; and there must be opportunity for the prospective teacher to view the acquisition of knowledge and the teaching of that knowledge to students as a single element—or at least as two closely related elements—in his training for teaching. Under this system the customary education courses would give way to organized experiences with students, experiences in which prospective teachers do much of the work in developing their own learning units with the help of their students, and then try out immediately whatever curricular materials they have developed and whatever pedagogical principles they have learned. At the same time, the college courses in science would be taught in such a way as to foster independent thought and inquiry by the prospective teacher. Here, too, the education of students is considered to be the ultimate purpose of the education of teachers. In short, the professor would teach his students by the inductive method as he has seen that method used with high school students.

The place of the student-teaching experience must be given special attention in the education of science teachers. In his recent book on the preparation of teachers, James B. Conant has recommended that the practice teaching experience be accepted by teacher educators as the heart of the pre-service experience.[4] The science teacher's

---

[4] James B. Conant, *The Education of American Teachers* (New York: McGraw-Hill Book Company, 1963).

job requires that he have intimate knowledge of a wide variety of special techniques and skills. These vary from supervising the laboratory work of the students in his classes to guiding the creative activities of those gifted students who often find an outlet for their special interests and abilities in independent study and project work in science. In this role he must be thoroughly familiar with the laboratory techniques and materials being used, especially in matters where the students' safety is to be considered. For these reasons the science teachers' training must include extensive training in the methods and procedures of laboratory-centered instruction, followed by a period of service under the guiding hand of an expert teacher of considerable experience. The teaching of science in an adequate fashion today cannot be learned from textbooks alone.

CHAPTER VII

Remaining Problems In Secondary-School Science Education

When one reads accounts of the recent curriculum revisions in science in the high school, there is the temptation to assume that the world's problems in science education will soon be solved. In reality, these new developments have served to reveal the true magnitude of the problems which have always faced us. In many ways the task of educating children in science appears to be more difficult now as a result of the recent curriculum projects.

The new curricula for the high school described in earlier chapters have expressed in operational terms a philosophy of science education. But the testing of this philosophy has not been accomplished; in many cases, there has been no serious attempt even to state testable hypotheses. Even if we assume that the basic principles of these projects are valid, there remains the problem of smoothing out the educational process by extending the new ideas in curriculum both upward and downward from the high school, and of making the teaching and learning processes more efficient. This chapter will present a brief summary of some of the more important problems which remain.

How Do We Make the Abstract Concrete?

As has been shown in earlier chapters, perhaps the strongest theme in all of the new curriculum efforts is that science at the high school level should represent a more fundamental approach from a disciplinary standpoint than has been the case in the past. The emphasis in all of the new curricula has been on the development of the structure of the subject so that the student learns to assemble basic information into meaningful generalizations.

If the idea of presenting basic scientific information in pre-college courses is examined, several practical problems become evident, for it is generally true that science, as it becomes more fundamental, becomes more abstract as well. Thus any attempt to present basic science is liable to make the subject less tangible to the student. The problems which this creates in motivation and the applications of knowledge have been discussed in Chapter I, but there is yet another serious difficulty which the new curricula have not solved.

In essence, a presentation which emphasizes basic science means that the abstract must sometimes be developed independent of or precedent to the concrete. This, of course, is contrary to the way we have often insisted that it be done. It has been shown that the child's ability to make abstractions develops with age and that abstract concepts are better understood if they are used to relate concrete examples.

Actually, this problem has not been ignored in the new programs. In fact, the development of new science courses has become more a matter of "how to make the abstract concrete" than of teaching abstractions before the concrete. Curriculum producers have stretched their imaginations to invent situations from which abstractions might be derived. The ingenious laboratory exercises of the PSSC physics program are perhaps the best examples of such developments. The exceedingly high cost, by traditional textbook standards, of producing the new curricula is related to the fact that many topflight scientists and educators had to be separated from their regular jobs and given freedom to concentrate on the creation of such situations. The new curriculum projects have taught us that the production of science curricula of this type is not a trivial job.

Although the new curriculum efforts have produced many ingenious examples of making the abstract concrete, much work remains to be done in this area. For many years the highly difficult problem of creating meaningful situations into which to place science students will be an extremely fruitful area of research that will undoubtedly produce improvements in the prototype materials we are now using.

Do the Students Really Learn "The New Science"?

If there is any one matter related to the new curricula in science which provokes unanimous concern, it is that of evaluation. Despite considerable effort, there is very little agreement on what the new curricula do for the high school student. This is an alarming statement considering the millions of dollars which have been invested in the development of materials; but it is more an indictment of the state of the art of testing than of the quality of the new materials. A few ideas are now beginning to emerge as to reasonable procedures to be followed in evaluating new curricula.

The problem can be effectively pointed up by describing one method in which curricula should not be evaluated. Several years ago one of the professional journals reported an evaluative study involving two groups of students which were matched on as many criteria as possible.[1] One group was given the PSSC physics course and the other studied a course based on a well-known traditional physics text. The achievement of the two groups was then compared on the basis of performances on the Cooperative Physics Test, a widely-used, standardized test of physics achievement. When the data were analyzed, it was found that the traditional students had scored higher on the test than had the PSSC students. The general conclusion of the study was that the PSSC program had been shown to be inferior in this respect to the traditional physics course.

The publication of the study brought a deluge of criticism from all sides. It centered on the fact that one should not evaluate the PSSC physics program on the basis of a test designed to measure achievement in terms of the objectives of traditional physics. In short, since the PSSC program did not set out to teach the information which was tested by the Cooperative Physics Test, it is not reasonable to evaluate its success in terms of that test.

It can be seen from this example that to evaluate any curriculum one must have two things: a good idea of what the program is designed to do, and some measuring device which will determine the degree to which the students demonstrate the competencies called for. Unfortunately, in the case of all of the new curriculum projects in science, we do not have sufficient information on either.

When one examines the periodical literature for clear statements of the objectives of the new courses, a wide variety of opinions is found. Despite the fact that the statements are variations on a single theme—that of altering the student's way of attacking problems—they are by no means clear enough to allow for the building of reasonable measuring devices.

---

[1] Warren L. Hipsher, "Study of High School Physics Achievement," *The Science Teacher*, XXVIII, No. 6, October, 1961, pp. 36–37.

One reads that the new courses develop "problem-solving ability," "enquiry ability," "scientific literacy," "increase in the skills of the processes of science," and similar attitudes and values. The question remains as to just what is meant by these terms and, more importantly, how one determines whether the student has these abilities. The reasons for the apparent lack of a clear statement of objectives for the new programs are roundly debated, as is the desirability of stating precise objectives in advance of the development of curricular materials. But the important point is that no such statement exists, and this is one of the major factors which have produced an almost impossible situation with regard to evaluation.

The second aspect of the evaluation problem is the lack of adequate measuring instruments. The developers of the new project feel that their courses require, at least at an intuitive level, the use of higher mental processes than simply the ability to recall information. This means that even if adequate objectives were stated, they would not be easily measured. No present-day testing expert has stated with much confidence how one goes about devising a test to measure critical thinking. Unfortunately, terms such as critical thinking are often defined in terms of "that which a certain test measures."

Assuming that some reasonably valid set of objectives could be written and that it were possible to produce instruments which could measure these, the question of what this would prove would still remain. Curriculum construction consists essentially of some individual or group asserting that a certain body of content represents what students in a particular course should study. Evaluation of curricula consists of trying to determine whether the materials produced actually accomplish what the developers say they should. In the case of the new science curricula, not everyone agrees that the content selected is the most appropriate for high school science students. Thus even if these programs were found to accomplish what their authors say they are designed to accomplish, there still remains the philosophical question of whether this is really what high school science students should study.

In summary, then, there is a serious need for more accurate and useful definitions of the abilities which science courses should seek to develop in students, and for tests that measure the students' capacity to carry out high-level mental operations. These, coupled with the further development of the tools of statistics and data-processing techniques to enable researchers to deal with the complex problems of evaluation, are perhaps the most important needs to be met before real progress can be achieved in science education.

Provision for Ability Levels

All the recent developments in science curriculum construction were designed for the "average" student taking a given course. The PSSC course developers aimed their program at about the upper twenty-five percent of the high school population, precisely the group which studies physics in the American high school. CHEM Study and CBA chemistry are aimed at roughly the upper half of high school students, and BSCS biology at about the upper seventy-five percent. Despite the fact that the classroom testing of these materials has indicated that they were suitable for the levels indicated, there is no doubt that they are not well suited for the slower students. If the new courses fail to attract more students to the study of science in high school, it will not necessarily be an indictment of the new materials, but may very well be attributable to those responsible for curriculum in the schools for failing to provide adequately for a range of abilities and aptitudes. Furthermore, the situation would not be qualitatively different from that of traditional science materials, since they, too, generally fail to challenge all science students effectively.

A drop in science enrollment would simply verify the great need for science courses developed on the same rationale as the present programs but geared to students at the lower end of the scale. Some efforts in this direction have been made (particularly by the BSCS biology group) but these have been, for the most part, relatively poorly supported when compared with the materials for more typical students. In addition, not many of the top-level people who developed the original courses have participated in the work on the low-level courses. This lack of support and personnel is unfortunate because of the greater difficulty of producing good materials for the less talented students. One can take some hope, however, from recent developments which show a growing concern for the slower students.

An equally difficult problem, but one which is probably not so pressing, is that of science for the talented student. The problem of the overburdening of slow students by the present courses has a counterpart for the bright. The need here is for completely new programs developed from the same base as those already produced, but with increased rigor, possibly exceeding that of the present freshman courses at the college level.

There is another dimension of the problem of student ability which relates to the earlier question of evaluation. If it becomes possible to determine whether students in the new programs are actually gaining the knowledge and skills which the writers intended, certain important psychological patterns may be revealed. There is a likelihood that the present courses are not reaching some students on a basis entirely apart from such obvious factors as intelligence. It may very well be that there is more than one type of human mind in terms of one's ability to learn science, and that programs based upon the rationale of the courses recently developed do not reach all of the various psychological types. Should this be the case, it may become necessary to design completely new courses with different appeals to different types of students. This could result in three or four courses for a given science subject, different from one another in approach rather than simply in level of sophistication or rigor. Conceivably, future students will be grouped on the basis of measurable psychological characteristics in addition to intelligence, and the means of classifying students may be derived from our efforts to evaluate existing science courses.

Extension Upward and Downward

Perhaps the most difficult problem that high school teachers of the new science programs face is that of breaking old habits. By the time they reach the tenth grade, most students have become conditioned to interpret science courses in terms of their earlier experiences, which dealt, in most cases, almost entirely with the acquisition of a body of science-related information.

The student with an understanding of science courses as places where one learns facts about nature, and where performance is evaluated in terms of how many facts and formulas can be memorized, finds the transition to the new courses quite difficult. As a matter of fact, many potentially capable students never recover from their previous training; for them the difference between the new curricula and more traditional science courses consists in memorizing "new" facts rather than "old" facts. As has been emphasized in the earlier chapters, the "new" facts of today are just as susceptible to being supplanted as are those facts and ideas from the past which have not stood the test of time. In short, the quest for information represents only a small portion of what the new courses purport to do, and students who concentrate on this aspect are not deriving the full benefit from such programs.

Had the revolution in science teaching occurred from the bottom of the educational ladder upward, the problems of articulation with other parts of the curriculum would not be so severe. If the curriculum makers had begun with the kindergarten child and worked up to the high school years, an adequate foundation for a coordinated K-12 science program might now exist. For such reasons as interest, availability of financial support, and likelihood of success this was not done. Consequently, the new high school science curricula stand on a rather shaky foundation. As this is being written, several programs of improvement for elementary and junior high school science are underway. All are pursuing basically the same philosophy which is evident in the high school programs. When such courses become operational, it is to be hoped that much of the student trauma associated with the high school courses will be eliminated.

But when the new courses in science for elementary and junior high schools become widely used, there will almost certainly be the need for heavy revision, if not complete overhaul, of the new high school programs as they now exist. If one thing can be said for the curriculum efforts of the last ten years, it is that they have revealed that children are able to manage more sophisticated subject matter than was previously thought possibly. Although the new high school curricula of today may seem quite advanced, there is a real possibility that much of their present content will have been taught by the end of the junior high school science sequence of tomorrow.

The problems of the coordination of the various segments of the science curriculum extend upward as well as downward. Many of the students who have been successful in the new high school courses, and who have come to view science as something more than a collection of facts, are disappointed when they enter their first college-level science course. Paradoxically, though the developers of the new courses at the high school level came mostly from the colleges and universities, the teaching at those levels often tends to be antithetical to the philosophy of these courses. Freshman college and university courses, in many cases, are poorly organized and lacking in the philosophy of modern science. These courses often consist largely of a series of unrelated topics treated only by the lecture method and followed by exercises in which the student is asked to reproduce, almost on a word-for-word basis, the information he has learned. Only occasionally is the student given the opportunity to express his own ideas on the topic under study.

Several groups in the United States are now directing their attention to the improvement of science courses at the college level. The prime movers in all of these groups are attempting to build a philosophy which is compatible with that of the secondary programs into instruction at this level. Any new college level courses developed in the near future will undoubtedly show increased sophistication as well as a philosophical reorientation. And this will add to the pressures which the new elementary and junior high school science courses will create for still further improvement of the high school courses.

The Problem of Coordination and Integration

In the opinion of some educators and scientists, the development of the new high school courses halted a desirable trend which had got underway just prior to their emergence. That was the movement toward integration and coordination of the sciences. About ten years ago, a few school systems in the United States had begun to offer high school courses which were not labeled as biology, chemistry, or physics. These courses, some of which were quite sophisticated, were developed in an effort to show the relationships among the various sciences. It was recognized by those who worked on these courses that the "areas of gray" between the sciences were becoming increasingly large. The sciences of biochemistry, biophysics, physical chemistry, chemical physics, photo-biology, and others had already emerged, and many scientists were unable to identify with the traditional disciplines of science. With this trend within the sciences, it was felt that high school students should be encouraged to think in terms of science as a whole rather than considering it as a collection of separate disciplines.

But when the new curriculum programs emerged, the trend was reversed. Despite the fact that all of the new courses include topics which would have been considered to belong to another discipline a number of years ago, no real attempt is made in any of them to show the inter-connections of all of the sciences. (The Blue Version of the BSCS course with its bio-physical and bio-chemical overtones probably comes closest to this goal.)

Some people feel that teaching science today as a series of separate disciplines is a serious mistake. They point out that within the lifetime of the students now taking high school science, these barriers are likely to fall and that a curriculum made up of specialized courses will leave the students with a poor understanding of the nature and scope of science. The solution to this problem remains to be found; but it is urgent enough to justify the initiation of projects to build interdisciplinary science courses parallel to the present courses in the separate sciences.

The Development and Use of Aids to Teaching

Although the subject matter involved is somewhat different from the traditional, the recent efforts to renovate the high school science curriculum have been quite conservative from an educational point of view. The "package" making up the "typical" new curriculum is limited to a textbook, a laboratory manual, correlated reading materials, and films which, in some cases, are not really an integral part of the course. The developers of the new courses have chosen to ignore, for the most part, an aspect of education which may have a profound influence on teaching in the near future: automated instruction. The caution displayed to date by science curriculum workers in using programmed instruction, computerized instruction, audio-visual teaching methods, and similar devices may very well be justified at this point in history. Because of the newness of these techniques, efforts to use them have tended to be rather short-sighted and are often prompted by concerns for economy rather than for the improvement of instruction.

Perhaps the best examples of the revolutionary potential offered by automated instruction are to be found in the area of computer technology. Among these a current project at the Massachusetts Institute of Technology provides a most dramatic lesson.

Project MAC (Multiple Access Cognition) is an attempt to systematize knowledge in a wide variety of fields and to make it almost instantly available to individuals across the country. It is now possible for a man in Los Angeles to "talk" to the computer at the MIT Computer Center and receive answers to technical questions on subjects ranging from engineering to zoology.

As an illustration, suppose a naval engineer in San Diego, California, has a particularly knotty problem dealing with the design of a merchant ship hull. If this man has arranged for the services of Project MAC, he may turn to an instrument on his desk not unlike a telephone and dial the computer in Cambridge. He may then instruct the machine to operate on any of the several hundred programs on file. The specifics of his merchant ship problem are then fed into the computer 3,000 miles away; within minutes the typed answers to his questions emerge from the machine on his desk.

In essence, Project MAC demonstrates the fact that within a few years everyone needing the services of a computer will be able to use the most up-to-date models at very low cost. It means that one with little or no training in higher mathematics will be able to solve very complex equations providing he can identify his problem and is equipped with a connection to a computer. The fact that a researcher anywhere in the United States is able to dial computers located from Boston to Berkeley makes it clear that these kinds of capabilities are not visions of the far-off future.

Project MAC and similar ventures are educationally significant. The engineer who wrote the program for the Project MAC computer really "taught" his San Diego colleague to solve a problem which did not exist when the program was written. More important perhaps, the "lesson" is now permanently recorded and available to anyone needing that kind of help. Furthermore, the lesson can be given after the "teacher" has turned his attention to other matters. This means that computer technology holds the potential to make the best thinking in a given subject easily available to an almost unlimited audience. Before this goal can be fully realized, however, careful experiments are necessary to reveal the most efficient way to put computers to use. In addition, school administrators and teachers must be willing to conduct bold implementation experiments.

There are other educational implications of Project MAC. The computer, above all, is the means by which the routine aspects of calculations of all sorts can be carried out automatically. This does not mean, however, that the individual, say twenty-five years from now, will not have problems to solve. The problems of that era will surely be more difficult; and one cannot take advantage of a computer unless he understands in very precise terms the method of attack necessary to solve whatever problem he has in mind. In short, the man of the future will find it indispensable to think very carefully through a problem and to express its elements in computer language. This argues very strongly for an emphasis in education upon understanding as opposed to memorizing. It would seem sheer folly, for example, to place the main emphasis on the calculations involved in solving physics problems since the student will likely be able to use a machine to do these calculations, providing he can "tell" the machine what is to be done.

Perhaps one way of expressing the impact which computerized instruction is likely to have on education is to say that the potential for the individual to educate himself will become almost unlimited. It should be pointed out that this is not the same as saying that the teacher will be unnecessary in the educational system of the future. It does mean, however, that the teacher's role will be changed drastically. The teacher will certainly become the guider of the educational process rather than the source of it. The teacher of tomorrow must show the student how to educate himself. And this role is more difficult to play than the teacher's present one.

The potential of the computer to change teaching methods and remove the need for transmitting large volumes of information to students of science is perhaps the most dramatic of the new approaches to education now being developed. There are, however, a number of other interesting techniques on the horizon. Programmed instruction, which is closely allied to the computer approach, is now receiving a good deal of attention. The technology associated with audio-visual education, particularly that connected with student-operated audio-visual devices, is advancing very rapidly. Although breakthroughs in these areas are likely to be made by specialized personnel, anyone concerned about the problems of education should become familiar with the current work and should be prepared to adjust to serious changes in teaching—changes which will go well beyond the current revolution in science teaching.

Bibliography

Biological Science: An Inquiry Into Life (Yellow Version). New York: Harcourt, Brace & World Co., 1963.

Biological Science: Molecules to Man (Blue Version). Boston, Mass.: Houghton Mifflin Co., 1963.

Brandwein, Paul. *Research Problems in Biology: Investigations for Students.* (Series 1 and 2.) New York: Doubleday & Co., 1963.

Bruner, Jerome S. *The Process of Education.* Cambridge, Mass.: Harvard University Press, 1961.

CBA Newsletter. Chemical Bond Approach Project. Richmond, Indiana: Earlham College, February, 1961.

Chemical Systems. Chemical Bond Approach Project. New York: McGraw-Hill Book Co., 1964.

Chemistry, An Experimental Science. Chemical Education Materials Study. San Francisco: W. H. Freeman & Co., 1963.

Conant, James B. *The Education of American Teachers.* New York: McGraw-Hill Book Co., 1963.

ESCP Newsletter, NL-1 Earth Science Curriculum Project, Boulder, Colorado (October, 1963).

Ferris, Frederick L., Jr. "The Princeton Junior High School Science Project," *Journal of Research in Science Teaching,* I, No. 3 (1963), 281.

Ferris, Frederick L., Jr. ed. *Time, Space, and Matter.* Junior High School Science Project. Princeton, New Jersey: Princeton University, 1964.

Fowler, H. Seymour. *Secondary School Science Teaching Practices.* New York: Center for Applied Research in Education, 1964.

Gagne, Robert. "A Psychologist's Counsel on Curriculum Design," *Journal of Research in Science Teaching,* I (1963), 27–32.

Goodlad, John I. *School Curriculum Reform in the United States.* New York: The Fund for the Advancement of Education, March, 1964.

Heath, Robert W. "Pitfalls in the Evaluation of New Curricula," *CHEM Study Newsletter,* II, No. 1 (December, 1961).

Heath, Robert W. (ed.) *New Curricula.* New York: Harper & Row, 1964.

Heller, Robert L. "The Earth Science Curriculum Project—A Report of Progress," *Journal of Research in Science Teaching,* II, No. 4 (1964), 330.

High School Biology: BSCS Green Version. Chicago: Rand McNally & Co., 1963.

Hipsher, Warren L. "Study of High School Physics Achievement," *The Science Teacher,* XXVIII, No. 6 (October, 1961), 36–37.

Hurd, Paul deHart. "The New Curriculum Movement in Science," *The Science Teacher,* XXIX, No. 1 (February, 1962), 7–9.

Innovation and Experiment in Education, A Progress Report of the Panel on Educational Research and Development. (President's Science Advisory Committee.) Washington, D.C.: Government Printing Office, March, 1964.

Introductory Physical Science. Preliminary Edition. Watertown, Mass.: Physical Science Study Committee of Educational Services, Inc., 1964.

Kessen, William. "Statement of Purposes and Objectives of Science Education in School," *Journal of Research in Science Teaching,* II, No. 1 (1964), 3.

Mathematics and Science in U.S. Public Schools, Circular 533. Washington, D.C.: Office of Education, 1958, p. 2.

Mayer, Martin. *The Schools.* New York: Harper & Row, 1961.

Morrison, Phillip. "Experimenters in the Classroom," *Science,* CXXXVIII No. 3547 (December, 1962), 1307–1310.

Physical Science Study Committee. *Physics.* Boston: D. C. Heath & Co., 1960.

Physical Science Study Committee. *Physics* (First Annual Report), I, Preliminary Edition, 3.

Schwab, Joseph J. *Biology Teachers' Handbook.* New York: John Wiley & Sons, Inc., 1963.

Schwab, Joseph J. "Enquiry, the Science Teacher, and the Educator," *The Science Teacher* (October, 1960), p. 6.

"Secondary School Physics: The Physical Science Study Committee," *Review of the Secondary School Physics Program of the Physical Science Study Committee.* Watertown, Mass.: Educational Services Inc., 1959.

Strong, Lawrence E., and Wilson, M. Kent. "Chemical Bonds: A Central Theme for High School Chemistry," *Journal of Chemical Education,* XXXV (February, 1958), 56.

Tyler, Ralph W. "Forces Re-Directing Science Teaching," *The Science Teacher,* XXIX (October, 1962), 22–25.

Ulry, Orval L. "A Study of the Relationship Between Subjects Taken and Other Selected Factors for the Class of 1958, Maryland Public High Schools," *The Science Teacher,* XXVII, No. 5 (September, 1960), 23.

Woodring, Paul. *Introduction to American Education.* New York: Harcourt, Brace & World Co., 1965.

Index